THE OXFORD CANAL

INLAND WATERWAYS HISTORIES

Edited by Charles Hadfield

THE
OXFORD CANAL

HUGH J. COMPTON

With 30 plates and 16 text illustrations
including maps

DAVID & CHARLES

NEWTON ABBOT   LONDON
NORTH POMFRET (VT)   VANCOUVER

ISBN 0 7153 7238 6
Library of Congress Catalog Card Number: 76–54077

© Hugh J. Compton 1976

Set in 11 on 13pt Garamond
and printed in Great Britain
by Latimer Trend & Company Limited Plymouth
for David & Charles (Publishers) Limited
Brunel House   Newton Abbot   Devon

Published in the United States of America
by David & Charles Inc
North Pomfret   Vermont 05053   USA

Published in Canada
by Douglas David & Charles Limited
1875 Welch Street   North Vancouver   BC

Contents

CHAPTER 1

The Beginning

JAMES BRINDLEY (1716–72) stood before the examining committee of the House of Lords and mixed some clay with water, then proceeded to fashion it into a bowl, then fill it with water. By this means he ably demonstrated to his Lordships that puddle-clay would provide a seal with which to retain water in canals.

This son of a labourer was born at Tunstead, Staffordshire, about four miles north-east of Buxton. In spite of the poor circumstances of the family he was helped by his mother's efforts to gain a slender education. For some years in his teens he worked as a farm labourer and at this period his mechanical bent showed itself by his interest in water mills and their modelling. When seventeen years old, he was apprenticed to Abraham Bennett, a Macclesfield millwright, and being both conscientious and determined, he gained valuable experience in making machinery for mills, apart from showing great skill and inventiveness in his methods. Being a poor writer and reluctant to make notes of machinery that he saw he developed an unusual memory for details. This preoccupation with construction of machinery for use with water power established the foundation for his subsequent civil engineering triumphs in waterway projects.

The transport of goods in England at the start of the eighteenth century relied upon navigable rivers such as the Thames, Trent, Severn and Mersey and upon unmade-up roads used by stage waggons and pack horses. The movement of barges on the rivers was subject to delays due to floods and draughts and whilst the

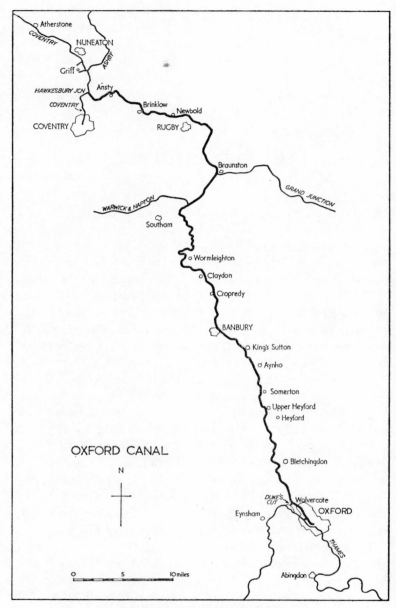

FIGURE I. Map of the Oxford canal

unit carried a substantial payload the same could not be said of the pack horse which at best had a few hundredweights. At this period roads were notoriously bad and often impassable in winter. The Industrial Revolution changed all this, canals were built to connect towns with rivers and turnpike trusts were set up to maintain the roads and charge for their use.

Francis sixth Earl and third Duke of Bridgewater (1736–1803), who owned a number of coal mines at Worsley north of Manchester, wished to increase the output of his mines and to find means to decrease the cost of transport as well as satisfying the ever-growing needs of the city of Manchester. Accordingly he promoted his canal in 1759 and by 1761 part of it was opened.

James Brindley, who had been working on the plans for the nearby Trent & Mersey, helped the duke on this project and by its success his capabilities were brought to the notice of other influential persons. He agreed with the suggestion that canals should be built to connect these four main rivers and this idea caught on and spread like a flame through the houses of the land. Josiah Wedgwood, the 'Prince of Potters' was responsible for the Trent & Mersey, designed by Brindley, and others thought of a branch to Coventry, this being in the general direction of the Thames. Thus by 1767 the people of the Midlands were involved; a meeting was held at Warwick on 18 August and whilst they agreed to the branch canal to Coventry they felt that perhaps it was a little too early to consider an extension from there via Banbury to the Thames Navigation at Oxford.

The promoters of the Coventry observing that work had started on the Trent & Mersey proceeded to obtain their Act of Parliament on 29 January 1768 and by 25 April construction work had started at the Coventry end.[1]

Sir Roger Newdigate (1719–1806) of Arbury Hall near Coventry, who besides being one of the promoters of the Coventry was also the MP for Oxford University and owned several coal mines, now saw that the time was ripe to take the first steps towards making the canal to Oxford. So on 13 April 1768, he visited Banbury in

Oxfordshire and talked with the Mayor and others about the proposed canal.[2] Afterwards, Brindley was requested to survey the proposed route and produce plans. In due course he completed his investigations and the results showed that at the Coventry end the junction with the Coventry was to be effected at Gosford Green, just outside the city, thence through the villages of Stoke and Bindley and on to Brinklow. This part of the canal involved a rise and fall of 64ft.

As in the case of the early railways, a number of landowners affected were opposed to the canal and therefore with a view to overcoming the objections of Lord Craven and Lord Denbigh, Sir Roger Newdigate wrote to Joseph Parker, surveyor and clerk of works to the Coventry asking him to survey a course of the canal from Bedworth via Ansty to Brinklow in order to avoid their lordships' objections.[3]

All these plans were duly submitted to the meeting which was chaired by Sir Roger Newdigate in the Three Tuns at Banbury on 25 October, and approved by the assembled company which included the Dukes of Marlborough and Buccleuch, the Lords Spencer, Guildford and North. Lord Craven and Lord Denbigh 'pronounced their disapprobation without one reason', after which the resolutions were voted on and £50,400 was subscribed. Thomas Walker, who besides being Oxford's town clerk was also a solicitor and clerk to the Oxford/Eynsham/Witney turnpike trustees and William Dadley, clerk to the Coventry were asked to prepare the Parliamentary Bill. These gentlemen together with Benjamin Aplin, Banbury's town clerk, were deputed to receive the money.[4]

Parliament on 29 November received the Petition in the House of Commons for the Bill duly supported by 'the Chancellor, Masters and Scholars, of the University of Oxford, the Corporation of the cities of Oxford, Coventry, the towns of Woodstock, Banbury and Daventry', together with several noblemen and others. Straightaway a Committee formed of Sir Roger Newdigate, who during February and March 1762 had been counsel in con-

nection with the proposed extension of the Bridgewater Canal
from Manchester to Liverpool, Lord Francis North (1704–90)
who was MP for Banbury from 1754 till his death, and others
were ordered to examine the Bill the same evening. A week later
Sir Roger Newdigate reported that Joseph Parker had examined
the route and 'thinks it is practicable' to make the canal. He mentioned that there were large quantities of limestone near part of
the canal which led from Newbold (near Rugby) to Oxford which
were at present useless for want of coal to burn it. Thomas Walker
was examined and stated that the roads in general were in bad
repair and in many parts impassable, but if the canal were built,
it would be a means of keeping the roads in much better repair.
The House then directed that Sir Roger, Lord North, Lord
Beauchamp, Lord Charles Spencer, Lord Wenman, Lord Robert
Spencer and others prepare the Bill.

On 4 February 1796, Sir Roger Newdigate went to Marlborough
House, London, to meet the dukes of Marlborough and Bridgewater, Lord Gower, Lord Charles Spencer, and others; in fact,
he made nearly forty visits seeking approval to the Bill.[5]

Whilst the landed gentry and others were doing their best for
the canal to Oxford, the opposition started to prepare their case.
The Chamber of London appointed a Committee to examine the
proposals and by mid-December reported that of the 80,000 tons
of coal moved west annually from London only about 3,000 tons
reached Oxford, though even this figure was an overstatement
since for 1767 it was 1,900 tons, only a further 50 tons going beyond. They thought that as the Newcastle coal was superior and
that coal coming from the Midlands would have to be transhipped
for travel over the Thames any loss of revenue would not greatly
affect London. Even so they recommended that a clause should
be inserted in the Bill to prohibit coal passing off the canal into
the Thames below Oxford. A realistic national view was adopted
on other matters; they agreed that the building of the canal would
generally be of great public advantage and instanced the fact that
the carriage of iron ex-Birmingham by land cost £5 per ton,

whereas by water it was expected to be reduced to £2.53. There was one point, however, which was to result in their proposed clause being inserted in the Bill, and that was the fear of reduced coal trade to London from the north-eastern coal mines which could result in a reduced number of colliers, whose seamen provided the main source of manpower for the Royal Navy in time of war.[6]

From February onwards Parliament received a number of Petitions on this aspect, notably from Scarborough, Whitby, Newcastle upon Tyne and Sunderland. George Perrott, the owner of the Lower Avon navigation which linked Evesham with the Severn petitioned also on the grounds that his revenue would be reduced because coal for Oxford, Chipping Norton and Woodstock which was landed at Evesham and Stratford-upon-Avon for onwards conveyance by waggon would pass instead over the intended Oxford. Tamworth, Lichfield and Birmingham, which had experience of canals, requested that the route from the Coventry be altered to avoid the lockage and in this they were supported by the Coventry who wanted the junction to be at Longford 4½ miles from Coventry which would result in the canal being on one level via Ansty and Shilton to Brinklow.

On 15 February the Bill came up for its second reading and Sir Roger, Mr Page and others were requested to examine it, Sir Richard Glynn being instructed to ensure that the junction at Longford, as requested by the Coventry, was in the Bill. The protagonists now began to drum up support. Banbury, Bicester and Brackley all sent in Petitions in support of the Bill; the users of the Avon Navigation petitioned against the Bill.

The following letter gives a very real insight into the needs for the canal so far as the wants of the local populace was concerned.

25 Feb 1769

I beg to ask the opposers of the navigation from Coventry to Oxford, whether they think of all the inconveniences they have pointed out, are equal to the starving to death many hundreds of poor inhabitants in the Inland Counties where coals may be brought by such a navigation? For I do take upon me to say, that were the Overseers of the poor ever so much disposed to show compassion to the poor, they have it now in their power to procure them fuel. There are many places near Banbury, Brackley, Bicester etc. where coals cannot possibly be had at any price to supply the necessary demand for them, where the strong and able poor have long subsisted by hedge-breaking; the wood is almost gone for fuel, which should grow for timber, there are no turbaries, and, in short, there are no materials by which the poor can procure even a wretched fire. In these parts, I believe they often perish by cold, though their cases do not appear in print; They are now dying (I may say like a rotten sheep) of putrid disease, possibly occasioned by their damp, cold comfortless dwellings. Ask physicians if this be an unreasonable suggestion! And they must have no fire foorsooth, to keep them alive, for fear Cheshire cheese should go to London by way of Oxford, or coals should be raised by ½p per cwt in Warwickshire. As the objections touching the coasting trade, they are absurd, groundless and calculated to serve private purposes, or borough purposes.[7]

Sir Roger Newdigate eventually reported to the House on 13 March that over fourteen meetings his Committee had examined the Bill and found it in order. The House ordered it to be printed and arrangements made for the East Coast shipping interests to be heard by the House. These were heard three days later after which a motion was put asking for the Bill to be delayed for three months. On a vote being taken this was defeated by 89 to 37. The House examined it again on 20 March. Due to pressure of business there was no time on the next day, so on 22 March a motion was carried to delay further investigation until 4 April. The following day it was passed by the Lower House and Sir Roger was requested to take it to the Lords. Since the Bill now had a clause inserted in it concerning the junction at Longford and another prohibiting coal onto the Thames below Oxford, the examining Committee of 45 Members including the Earls of Abingdon and Guildford who were appointed on 11 April, found that the spade work had been done in the House of Commons.

On 17 April Lord Viscount Say and Sele of Broughton Castle near Banbury reported on the Bill and two days later they passed it. King George III was pleased to give it the Royal Assent on 21 April 1769 and thus the Oxford was born in the same year as Napoleon Bonaparte.[8]

The Act stated that the canal would be routed through Ansty, Shilton, Brinklow, Newbold, Hillmorton, Braunston, Napton, Wormleighton, Cropredy, Banbury, King's Sutton, Aynho, Souldern, Heyford, Shipton, Thrupp and Wolvercote to Oxford. Whilst no specific branches were authorised by the Act it nevertheless allowed the construction of branches to any quarry or pit of limestone providing that it was within five miles of the canal and that two-thirds of the owners through whose land the canal would pass agreed to it. Water supply with a canal is always an important item for consideration and to ensure that supplies for the Oxford were adequate it allowed the proprietors to take any water found within five miles of the canal on the long summit pound over the Chiltern Hills north of Banbury. As usual with Canal Acts it was very specific with regard to money. The capital was to consist of 1,500 £100 shares of which no more than 50 were to be owned by any one person. Five per cent could be paid on shares till the canal was completed and if the need arose another £50,000 could be raised as well.

Even the management of the canal was specified. The General Assembly was not restricted as to its meeting point, but the three committees to be appointed to run the canal were very clearly defined. The section within Warwickshire from the junction with the Coventry at Longford to Wormleighton was to be controlled from Coventry. This was easily the biggest section and until work on it was finished it was no use starting on the other portions. Oxfordshire had two committees: one controlling the Wormleighton–Aynho section was to meet at Banbury, and the other, the last piece from Aynho to Oxford, was to meet at Oxford.

So that the canal did not abuse the traders who wished to use it, by overcharging them (having regard to the greatly improved means of transport being provided), the Act stipulated that the maximum rate was to be ½d per ton per mile. The roads whose condition Thomas Walker commented upon unfavourably, were given a fillip in as much as material for their use was to travel free. The Coventry, who had got the junction altered, prevailed upon the House to insert a curious clause in the Act to the effect that coal traffic for the first two miles on the Oxford were to pay the toll to the Coventry to equate for the lost mileage over the Coventry since the coal mines were situated at or near the agreed junction. Conversely the Oxford were to receive the tolls on merchandise traffic for the three and one half miles from Coventry because of the extra distance that they had to travel over the Coventry. Failure to comply with the prohibition on the carriage of coal beyond Oxford down river, which had been put in at the behest of the 'sea coal' interests, could result in forfeiture of the vessel and cargo together with a fine of £50.

Meanwhile Brindley, following a meeting on 14 February, had started to inspect the ground for cutting the canal and on 12 May was present at the first meeting of the canal company held in the Three Tuns at Banbury. The taking of subscriptions was completed at this meeting when James Brindley subscribed £2,000. Of the 1,500 shares issued no less than 901 were taken up by people in Oxford. These included 20 to Dr Nathan Wetherell (1726–1807), Vice-Chancellor of the University, 10 to the Rev David Durell (1728–75) and 18 to the City Council. Other important shareholders were:

Duke of Marlborough —	50 shares
Marquis of Blandford —	50 ,,
R. Newdigate —	20 ,,
F. Page —	20 ,,
Lord C. Spencer —	20 ,,
Lord R. Spencer —	20 ,,
T. Walker —	10 ,,
R. Parrott —	10 ,,
Duke of Buccleuch —	10 ,,
C. Nourse —	10 ,,

Lord F. Rowdon	— 10 shares	
R. Tawney	— 10 ,,	
B. Aplin	— 10 ,,	
Earl Harcourt	— 10 ,,	[9]

By this time Brindley had been appointed engineer and general surveyor at £200 per annum with James King as his clerk of works and Samuel Simcock as assistant. Bricklayers and a carpenter were sent to canal work in Staffordshire 'for their improvement'. It was decided that the accounts for the company should be kept in a mercantile manner by double entry, and notices of calls were to be put not only in newspapers but on church doors, where the many clergymen shareholders would see it.

The financial arrangements made by the Oxford in 1769 were as follows. Of the three local treasurers appointed to manage the finances of the different stretches of the line, only one, Thomas Little of Coventry, a promoter of the Oxford, was a banker; his partner, John Lowke, was a mercer, and by 1784 Little had been appointed one of the receivers-general of the land-tax for Warwickshire. This firm later became Little Woodcock who in 1865 amalgamated with the Birmingham banking group which in turn was absorbed by the Midland Bank in 1914. The Oxford treasurer was Thomas Walker, who held the receivership for the county of Oxford. He subsequently became a banker. The Banbury treasurer was at first a local solicitor, Benjamin Aplin, but he resigned after six months, because he received no official compensation for his services. His funds were transferred to Little; when another Banbury treasurer was appointed the choice fell on a Mr Calcot, a stationer, who happened to be also the local distributor of stamps. The inference is plain: Walker, Calcot, and Little were able to obtain their 'compensation' as treasurers by employing the Oxford's funds in their general business.[10]

Brindley finally completed his plans and at a meeting in the Three Tuns on 3 August the company agreed to them by 744 to 45. Next month cutting started at Conly Lane, Longford and by 18 November *Jackson's Oxford Journal* reported that the first mile

Plate 1 Near Ansty. Narrow boats with coal released after a stoppage caused by ice

Plate 2 The eastern portal of the first tunnel at Newbold

Plate 3 Narrow boats *Dipper* and *Bordesley* of the Willow Wren carrying company moored near Rugby, 1970, on a part of the canal opened in 1834

Plate 4 Horse-drawn narrow boat passing the building of the Great Central railway bridge near Clifton in about 1895. Bridge demolished 1975

of the canal was nearly finished. The northern section committee who met in the White Bear Inn at Coventry appeared to be doing well, thanks to Sir Roger who was their chairman, and William Dadley their clerk.

The clause which resulted in the junction being placed at Longford necessitated the Coventry and Oxford being parallel for one mile and in November the Oxford suggested a more sensible junction at Hawkesbury. The Coventry were willing provided the Oxford would pay a compensation toll on the two miles lost and also their legal fees of £150, to which the Oxford objected.

A far-reaching decision was, however, made in the George Inn at Lichfield on 14 December when all the canals being built or already constructed in the Midlands met and agreed to standardise their locks to enable boats of 74ft 9in × 7ft × 4ft 4in to pass. So the gauge of the narrow canal system was set, of which the Oxford was a part.

With a comfortable balance of £3,277 about 700 men were employed in cutting the canal and orders were given for the purchase of two maintenance boats. The canal was being built with a bottom width of 16ft which was just sufficient to enable two 7ft wide narrow boats to pass. The depth of water was 5ft and 1ft above the water level was the towing path 7ft wide.

The first 10 miles of the canal was completed by March 1771 and at last the company were able to take their first tolls.

Brindley, who had a hand in the making of no less than 365 miles of canals, passed away on 27 September 1772, at his Staffordshire home. Of him Samuel Smiles the biographer wrote:

> We doubt whether mere hard work ever killed any man or whether Brindley's labours, extraordinary though they were would have shortened his life, but for the far more trying condition of the engineer's vocation—irregular living, exposure in all weathers, long fasting, and then, perhaps, heavy feeding when the nervous system was exhausted, together with the habitual disregard of the ordinary conditions of physical health.

In his place Samuel Simcock, his assistant, whose wife Esther was

B

the sister of James Brindley, was appointed at the same salary of £200 per annum.

The wisdom of allowing further capital to be raised under the Act now became apparent, since works were costing more than anticipated. In consequence in 1774 when nearly 40 miles of the canal was opened to Napton from which point coal was being sent on by land carriage to Oxford, Banbury, Bicester and Woodstock etc, it was agreed at a meeting on 4 July following a report by Simcock that further sums were necessary and straight-away over £13,000 was subscribed.[11]

The local Oxford paper was full of praise for the coals from Hawkesbury pit saying 'they require no stirring as is necessary for sealcoal; but being put on the fire, and suffered to lie at rest, makes an exceedingly cheerful fire, and burns till the whole is consumed to ashes without further trouble!'

But the limits for raising capital under the Act were soon exhausted and accordingly on 20 March 1775 the company obtained a further Act by which they were allowed to borrow £70,000 for completion of the canal to Banbury.[12] They thought that only £30,000 would be required, but obviously they were cautious and got permission for more. No doubt the swift passage of the Bill was greatly facilitated by the fact that one of their shareholders, Lord North the MP for Banbury, was prime minister. By August £11,900 had been raised at 4½ per cent interest, the largest investors being the Duke of Marlborough and Charles Nourse who each advanced £2,000; this amount was sufficient to allow the works to proceed.[13] Under this Act the safety of the works in the area of the coalfields was guarded by a clause which prohibited the mining of coal under the canal or indeed within 12yd of it unless tunnels were used whose dimensions were not more than 6ft × 4ft. To prevent the influential proprietors of the canal suiting themselves as to the venue for the General Assembly, the Act stipulated that it should be in the Three Tuns at Banbury.

It is not surprising that the money had run out since the company had been involved in two major engineering works.

Brindley had achieved great fame on the Bridgewater Canal when he had built the Barton aqueduct over the river Mersey which was ridiculed by his contemporaries as being a 'castle in the air'.

Eleven miles from Longford at Brinklow he used this experience to design an aqueduct which was built at a cost of £12,000. This magnificent structure consisted of twelve arches, each of 22ft span built of square stones and bricks, and was connected to a 600ft embankment at one end and a 400ft embankment at the other.[14] As built, the twelve arches were used as follows—one was over a stream and two kept as passages. The keeper occupied one, the next was used as a stable, the next as a store room for hay and straw, and the next as a forge, the remainder being intended for dwellings, rather like the original idea for the London & Greenwich Railway viaduct, though whether they were lived in is doubtful.

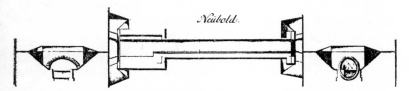

FIGURE 2. Plan of first tunnel and portals at Newbold, 1777

Seven miles on the company built the small tunnel at Newbold, though not as originally intended. During the construction they formed the opinion that if the tunnel by the church was of the normal design, there was a very real danger that the church would subside. Accordingly they altered the design and built it in two different styles. The west part was 104ft long and made with a roof like the arch of a normal canal bridge with a 5ft wide towing path. The east part was 308ft long, but only 11ft wide which included a 3ft wide towing path with a wooden railing.[15] This somewhat unusual elliptical design gave only 14ft for height of which 5ft was water. This 412ft tunnel was used till 1834.

Now that there was plenty of money available work began

again in earnest and by May 1776 the canal had reached Fenny
Compton. As the length of the canal increased so did the chance
of taking tolls, since the owners of waggons had to travel less
distance from the towns which they served. Even at that time
those in the know must surely have had an inkling of the great
wealth to come since even though the canal was not as yet
connected to any other system it was nevertheless making a profit
of £206.25 per week.

The saga of the junction with the Coventry was still far from
complete, for the changes in the Act had still to be carried out.
The Coventry had had some money troubles too which resulted
in their progress being rather tardy. This fact had annoyed the
Oxford so much so that in 1773 when meeting in Banbury they
seriously considered extending their canal by 31 miles to Birmingham at an estimated cost of £103,000. In December they
approved the plan and sent it to the Birmingham for comment.
This meeting had been held in the Star at Oxford, which subsequently became the Clarendon Hotel and is now one of F. W.
Woolworth's stores. Their plan did not meet with approval so it
was dropped. Fortunately for the Oxford their canal started in a
coal mining area so they were able to supply most of their line
from the pits at Hawkesbury and Wyken. Further supplies from
Bedworth and points on the Coventry necessitated transport by
waggon. The compensation tolls were the root cause why the
Coventry and the Oxford had not affected a junction earlier. The
Oxford people had tried many ways to overcome the peculiar
method of charging which the Act required, even going so far as
suggesting the junction be made elsewhere, perhaps at Bedworth,
but all to no avail. Eventually in May 1776 the Oxford agreed to
the Coventry's proposal that the junction should be completed
forthwith on the clear understanding that 'no coals or other com-
modities shall with their knowledge, permission or convenience
pass out of one canal into the other but by the point of such
junction'. Furthermore the Coventry promised extension to
Fradley, intended point for joining with the Trent & Mersey, as

soon as possible. However things are not always as easy as seem at first since in this draft agreement was a clause to the effect that the Oxford would pay the compensation toll for the two miles lost (Longford–Hawkesbury and return) for only the next seven years unless the Coventry were completed to Fradley, and would cease to pay it altogether when the Coventry made connections with the Staffordshire collieries.

This in turn did not come to fruition, so the Coventry sought a mandamus (superior court's writ) to compel the Oxford to complete the junction as required by Parliament. The treatment worked. The Court of King's Bench made an order, and on 15 April 1777 the junction at Longford was effected, the Coventry providing the toll-house at a cost of £75.60.

Both canals were supposed to be on the same level, but the making of the junction showed in fact that there was a difference of 6⅞in, which was enough to ensure the building of a lock and what was of more importance to canal engineers, the continued loss of water from the Oxford to the Coventry.

The Oxford, like the Coventry, was far from complete. Moreover, the two canals though now connected were not linked to any other major waterways. The Coventry at this time stretched on a level line from Coventry to Atherstone, a distance of only 15 miles. Four and a half miles from Coventry was the junction with the Oxford with which it ran parallel for a mile; another mile on was the junction with the Coventry Communication canal built by Sir Roger Newdigate to serve his collieries, and five miles beyond was Nuneaton. These canals though small did however serve a number of collieries and quite a number of people. This part of the self-contained system was to remain unaltered for a number of years, the next addition came in 1786 when Sir Roger Newdigate opened his Griff Hollow canal which joined the Coventry half-way between the Coventry Communication canal and Nuneaton.[16] In 1782 the promoters of a canal from Ashby Wolds by way of Market Bosworth and Hinckley had given notice of making a canal to join the Coventry at the same place, but it was not till 1792 that this project finally got under way.

On the Oxford things were really taking shape, for an agent had been appointed at Hawkesbury colliery wharf who was paid 60p per week. This wage compared favourably with that of a labourer's 40–50p at this period. Highwaymen and other bandits were common so two pistols were ordered for use by the company's agents. Special rates were quoted for corn or meal in 20 ton lots from Hawkesbury to Hillmorton at £2.10, and it was agreed that coal from any colliery was to pass at the same rate. To obtain these special concessionary rates application had to be made to Thomas Carpenter who held a post called 'Paymaster to the Company Proprietors'. A warehouse had been built at Hillmorton and let for £18 per annum.

Sir Roger Newdigate who had done so much for canals received a complaint from the trustees of a turnpike that the canal company's agents were refusing to allow materials for making up roads to pass free of tolls as prescribed by the Act of Parliament. However on the basis that the Act did not say when, the canal company interpreted it to their own advantage by saying the boats could only pass when there was surplus water, ie, when the water was flowing out of the canal, over the weirs.

In the section from Napton to Banbury the company had to construct a large tunnel at Fenny Compton. This brick-built tunnel was 1,138yd long, 12ft high and 9ft wide. To assist the passage of boats there were wooden blocks with iron rings every 12ft on both sides and every so often passing points 16ft wide. The boatmen took hold of these rings with their hands and pulled themselves from one to another.[17]

The building of this tunnel, sometimes called a 'Walled Underground Canal', took the usual form. After the lie of the land had been studied, shafts were sunk for the full width of the canal until the base line was reached. Then they were worked in a horizontal direction until meeting. The spoil was taken to the surface with the help of a hoist in buckets or barrels, and as soon as possible the rough bore of the tunnel was strengthened with wood.

On 4 April 1774 the General Assembly discussed the water supply required for the summit pound and asked either Thomas Yeoman or John Smeaton, both well-known engineers, to agree a date on which with Simcock he could view the top pound and recommend what action would be required. On 4 July Yeoman reported that Byfield water (lower part of present-day Boddington reservoir) in Northamptonshire would cost £750 and should be able to supply 35 locks of water in a dry day. To make further provision he suggested that the 11 mile long summit pound should be made ½yd deeper to provide a further four locks of water per day for fifteen weeks at an extra cost of £1,000. All these proposals were agreed and a subscription for £30,000 was opened and straightaway taken up, the first calls being made on 12 August. This money was soon put to good use in the making of a second and bigger reservoir at Clattercote in Oxfordshire situated 5¼ miles due north of Banbury.

The land for this reservoir was purchased from Thomas Cartwright one of the canal shareholders who had secured an undertaking from the company that the sluice be set 4ft above the bottom of the pool to preserve the fishing in a dry season, but alas the undertaking was not kept.[18] The feeder from the reservoir traverses over two miles and in this distance there is a tunnel of 869yd, during the descent from the level of 425ft at the reservoir to 389ft at the summit level of the canal. Later in 1787 the reservoir was enlarged at a cost of £1,373 and then held 3,222 locks of water.

Work on cutting the canal pressed ahead with considerable vigour and by November 1776 they had started cutting within 2 miles of Banbury. As soon as water was let into the canal boats laden with coal followed and on 1 October 1777 it was announced in *Jackson's Oxford Journal* that the wharf at Cropredy was opened and coal was available for sale at 5p per cwt.

At long last the initial goal of the Oxford was reached when on 30 March 1778 the first freight of about two hundred tons of coal was ushered into the wharf at Banbury amidst the loudest acclamations of a prodigious number of spectators and the day was spent in festivities including a dinner at the Three Tuns. Coal was sold at the wharf at 5p per cwt or 4½p to persons carrying it by waggon to any place over 14 miles from Banbury.[19]

Sir Roger Newdigate was soon making use of this facility since in June it was announced that 'the best Griff coals belonging to Sir Roger Newdigate are sold at the wharf by Mr Eaton'.

The 1769 Act allowed the movement of pleasure boats free between locks as long as they did not traverse more than two miles of the waterway. There is no record of any person making use of this facility, but Sir Roger Newdigate did the thing in style, for on 22 September 1778, accompanied by his wife Hester and his agent Thomas Hutchins, he embarked on the 'Hester Barge' at Griff Hills bridge and journeyed by way of the Coventry and Oxford canals reaching Stretton wharf at 8 pm where the party were met by coach and conveyed to Newnham Hall as the guests of Lord Denbigh for the night.

Next morning (23 September) the coach took them back to Stretton wharf with Lord Denbigh, Mr C. Fielding and Miss Carpenter who went as far as Brownsover in the boat. They dined at Hillmorton aboard and then proceeded as far as Napton where they were met and taken to Ladbroke, the boat was taken on by its crew as far as Fenny Compton.

Leaving Ladbroke next day in Mrs Palmer's chaise and accompanied by Charles Palmer and his wife in another chaise from Banbury they embarked on the boat at Fenny Compton and proceeded to Banbury where they dined aboard. The party then returned to Fenny Compton and inspected 'ye great Tunnell', and returned to Ladbroke where they stayed the night.

On 25 September they returned to Fenny Compton and re-embarking had breakfast on the boat with Charles Palmer and his wife who accompanied them as far as Napton. Dinner was taken aboard as they proceeded back to Brownsover where Lord Denbigh's coach met them and took them on to Newnham, the boat following to Stretton wharf.

Next morning a coach took the party to Stretton to join the boat. Dinner was taken aboard during the journey back to Griff Hill where they drank coffee and then took the coach back to Arbury Hall.

One further voyage at this early date is worth recording and that was a journey from Banbury to Arbury by Charles Parker and Mrs Kempson in a canoe. They were met at the lodges by Sir Roger Newdigate on 10 August 1779.[20]

The canal had now been made for a distance of 63¾ miles and had cost £205,148.22 as will be seen from the undermentioned statement:

	£	p
Coals used by Canal Co	1,439.	36
Coals sold by Canal Co	18,870.	25
Sundries	4,334.	84
Officers' Salaries	3,897.	15
Damages	1,717.	00
Travelling Expenses	212.	35
Horses	150.	42
Horse keeping & Waggons	472.	67
Boating	4,814.	33
Carriage	14,678.	98
Blacksmith	1,350.	52
Wheelbarrows	1,061.	37
Deals and planks	1,935.	65
Posts and rails	5,118.	16
Quicking (Hedges)	1,305.	53
Carpentry, Sawing, Boat Building	6,696.	88
Woodwork	210.	76
Timber	10,253.	83
Lime	4,545.	71
Brickmaking, bricks bought and casting clay	11,339.	29
Bridges and brickwork	7,379.	97
Ironmonger	2,072.	41
Stone digging and mason's work	4,631.	69
Day Labour	20,518.	76
Cutting canal culverts and puddling etc	43,387.	91
Land purchased	26,413.	97
Land rents	565.	34

	£	p
Tunnelling	2,781.	01
Repairs	2,991.	11
GRAND TOTAL	£205,148.	22[21]

This canal had been built to a typical Brindley specification by following the contours of the hills and valleys and so its winding course added many miles to the distance between principal places; in fact at Brinklow it was said that a boatman could be on the move all day and still hear the chimes of the church.

The bridges on this part of the canal were mainly built of brick except the top walls and the edge of the arches; underneath was a towing path. The canal so far completed had 144 waggon bridges, 13 swing bridges and 10 footbridges. In addition there were 44 bridges over the two feeders.

At this stage it only employed 25 men on the works, but already 100 boats were using the navigation including 47 owned by the canal company, some of which were hired out to Sir Roger Newdigate.[22] The inventory for 1778 includes among other items a machine for raising boats, pile driving and ice breaking, a timber carriage waggon, two rolling carts, a pleasure boat, two floats and a variety of tools many of which are not in use today.

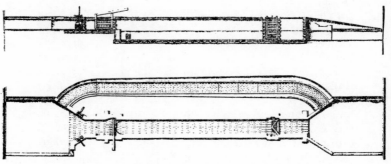

FIGURE 3.   Side and plan view of early lock, 1777

The locks on this section of the canal were 8oft long between heel posts and 7¼ft wide, usually built of brick with stone on the corners and slopes. As originally built there was a piece of wood or iron protruding from the walls to prevent them being damaged by the boats. At the bottom of the lock was a grid which was secured with posts according to the condition of the foundation and over this there was a double layer of planks. The locks had a single top gate and two bottom gates with 2ft high sluices. It took three to four minutes to fill with nearly 4,500 cubic feet of water, so a boat could easily pass through in nine to ten minutes. The cost of each lock was about £300.[23]

CHAPTER 2

And so to Oxford

KING CHARLES I, who had been using Oxford as his capital since the battle of Edgehill in 1642, was finding great difficulty in getting his supplies through. For the Roundheads were preventing movement on the River Thames from below Wallingford and from above Eynsham. The Cherwell and its tributaries at this time were not navigable but Charles wanted to make them suitable for the bringing in of supplies from the north-east.

Whereas we are informed that there are divers impediments upon the Rivers Cherwell, Ottmore and Ray, that hinder the passing of boats to and from Bicester and Blackthorn (Ambrosden) and this our city of Oxford, to the great damage of the inhabitants of this our County and City, which may be remedied by altering and removing Bridges, Mills and Weirs at a very small charge, and will prove of great advantage to the poor Subjects of this our County; our will and pleasure therefore is, and we do hereby authorise you, immediately upon sight thereof to repair to the said rivers, and that you cause all the said Bridges, Mills, Weirs and other impediments upon the said rivers to be removed or altered according as the necessity of the service shall require, and you may cut down trees as you require in Merton Woods, for making Boards, Planks, and Joists for repairing or altering the bridges, and weirs taking care that no unnecessary damage is caused during the work; willing and requiring the Governors of the City of Oxford all Commanders and Officers of our Army, Sheriffs and Justices of the Peace, and all other Officers to aid and assist you in passing carts, Teams, Boats and Workmen, and to contribute their help in all such matters as may be necessary and requisite for perfecting the works, and this is your Warrant.

Given at our Court at Oxford 11th February, 1644.
By His Majesty's Command
George Digby
To our trusty and wellbeloved
Francis Mildmay and Hugh Gore[1]

It is very doubtful whether in fact any works were actually carried out.

Some 33 years later Andrew Yarranton, who began life as a linen-draper's apprentice and became, successively, a captain in the parliamentary (Roundhead) army, a farmer and the owner of iron works in Worcester; wrote a book in 1677 following a visit to Holland and France. In it he drew attention to the neglected condition of the Thames between London and Oxford, comparing the Metropolis to the heart, and the rivers to the veins of the body, and advocating the improvement of the Thames and Cherwell. Drawing upon his experience with the Worcestershire Stour which he had made navigable between 1665 and 1667, he suggested two schemes for the River Cherwell.

One involved making the Cherwell navigable between Oxford and Banbury at an estimated cost of £10,000, the idea being that at Banbury waggons could connect with Shipston, situated on a tributary of the Warwickshire Avon, and thus provide a link between the Thames and Severn rivers. The other suggestion was to make the Cherwell navigable as far as Aynho at a cost of £2,500. On the navigation four granaries for £6,000 each were to be built capable of holding 14,000qr of corn together with mills and twenty houses for the employees.[2]

His first scheme must have been carried out, even though there was no supporting Act of Parliament, since in the Banbury register of births and deaths it is recorded that John Barnes, a waterman, died there on 22 March 1693 and similarly Thomas C. Gasgoigne on 21 July 1706. More important evidence however is that Sanderson Miller (1673–1737), a merchant at Banbury, who was mayor in 1707 and an alderman from 1710 to 1714, brought his goods from Oxford to Banbury in flat-bottomed boats designed by himself.[3]

Two experimental trips were made in 1764, which would have greatly interested King Charles. In the first one a barge loaded with coal left Oxford on a Tuesday morning in January and travelled first up the Cherwell to Islip and then along the old River Ray arriving on the following morning at Lower Arncott Bridge. From there the coals were carried one mile in wheelbarrows to Ambrosden Park, the seat of Sir Edward Turner, Bart.

> The Bargemen, having been plentifully regaled at Sir Edward's till Thursday morning, returned here (Oxford) in nine hours, the barge being freighted with barley. From this attempt it is found practicable to open a navigation from Oxford to that place and much further northward . . . Could such a scheme of this nature be put into execution the advantages arising therefrom are too conspicious to need explanation.[4]

The second trip took place in early February when a light vessel in ballast with a certain Captain Toovey accompanied by two gentlemen set sail from New Quay, Holywell mill by Napper's bridge just north of Oxford and proceeded to Bicester (13 miles by road from Oxford). The local paper stated: 'This vessel is gone to make observations on that new discovered passage. She went off with a fair wind and is expected to run it at the rate of ten knots an hour.' Unfortunately, this is the only reference and what actually happened is not known.

The Cherwell was still navigable for 13 miles up to Shipton-on-Cherwell in 1777; the decline northwards was no doubt due to the Banbury–Oxford road being improved under the turnpike Act of 1755.[5]

Although the Oxford company had powers to construct the canal southwards from Banbury to Oxford it had reached the financial limits of its previous Act and therefore it was necessary to obtain an accurate survey on which detailed costs could be based.

In January 1779 accordingly the company asked two people whether they would carry out the desired survey—John Gilbert (1724–95), who supervised the building of the Bridgewater, and Robert Whitworth who had done some of the earlier survey work for the Oxford. John Gilbert declined and instead Samuel Simcock took his place.

Not only had work stopped on the Oxford, but also on the Coventry and in consequence the desired connection between the Mersey and Thames rivers had not been made at either end. Shortage of money was at the root of the problem for in the year ending August 1780, out of earnings of £6,982, no less than £3,149 was paid out as interest on loans. So it was essential to convince investors that the completion of the authorised works would produce adequate financial reward.

The representatives of the various canals concerned all met at Coleshill in Warwickshire on 20 June 1782 and agreed a scheme which was subsequently ratified by the canal companies on 29 October 1783. By this the Oxford agreed to continue its line for the 27½ miles to Oxford, and the Trent & Mersey in conjunction with the Birmingham & Fazeley agreed to take over the Coventry's rights so that the latter could be constructed by them beyond the Birmingham & Fazeley to the junction with the Trent & Mersey.

It was one thing for the Oxford to make this agreement; it was quite another matter to find the money. In the following year the financial position was so bad that the Duke of Marlborough paid the interest due to the creditors.[6]

Finally in September 1785 the Oxford made two important moves. Samuel Weston was asked to make a survey of the River Cherwell from Banbury to Oxford and at the same time advertisements were placed in the local papers stating that the Oxford intended to apply for parliamentary powers to make the Cherwell navigable to its junction with the Thames. Samuel Weston's survey must have been satisfactory since in February 1786 he was told to ask the landowners and occupiers of land between Oxford and Banbury for their consent to making a towing path along the banks of the Cherwell.

However, the Oxford changed its mind about the line of the canal and in the Bill to Parliament the 1769 route was again repeated. The Bill, prepared by Francis Page (of the Kennet Navigation), Sir William Dolben and Sir Charles Spencer, was introduced into the House of Commons on 3 March 1768. Thomas Walker, on behalf of the company, answered many points put by Members on 17 March.

The Petitioners against the Bill were heard on 30 March and as a result the undermentioned two clauses were deleted:

(a) No boat to navigate any part of the canal between Banbury and Oxford until the whole canal is completed, without permission of the canal company.
(b) Oxford Canal Company to be allowed to decide when land taken for canal whether payment is to be made in a gross sum or by annual rent.

Following its successful passage through the House of Lords it received the Royal Assent on 11 April.

The Act allowed a further £60,000 to be borrowed, but the dividend was not to exceed 4 per cent till the canal was finished and half of the borrowed capital repaid.[7] Thereafter the limit was to be 5 per cent until the rest of the money borrowed had been paid off. Other important sections were the deletion of the clause in the 1769 Act prohibiting the movement of coal down the river Thames from Oxford, and the inclusion of a clause permitting the Oxford to use any water found within 1,000yd of the canal together with the user of the Churchover stream in Cosford valley near Rugby.

The Coventry kept its part of the agreement by obtaining an Act in 1786 which authorised the Trent & Mersey and Birmingham & Fazeley to complete the line, and also there was a clause which limited the rates for the first two miles on the Coventry and Oxford which were collected by the opposite company under the 1769 Act.[8]

Plate 5 Hillmorton middle locks about 1910 with coal fired narrow boat

Plate 6 Wolfhampcote tunnel in 1972. This short tunnel became disused when the line of the canal was shortened in 1834

Plate 7 Grand Junction canal company's marker erected between Napton and Braunston when the company assumed responsibility for the maintenance of this section

Plate 8 The opening of the Fenny Compton Tunnel of the Oxford canal. View showing the elevation of an aqueduct or trunk 'for connecting the collecting feeder to the Wormleighton Reservoir', formed with wrought iron riveted plates and carried across the canal by two brick piers (1869)

The line of the Oxford was now marked out under the super-
vision of the resident engineer, James Barnes (1740–1819). In
January 1787 arrangements were made for Mr Creek to see representatives of landowners through whose ground it was intended to cut the canal with a view to having the land valued.
Robert Whitworth in surveying the final line had decided that
the canal should not cross the Cherwell twice on an aqueduct.
Instead, through Heyford, half way between Banbury and Oxford, about a mile of the Cherwell near the Manor House was to
be used for the canal and a new channel dug for the river. In
1790 this change resulted in legal proceedings when Thomas
Rose brought an action against the Oxford's contractors, Henry
Baker and Henry Golding, for diverting the river. The Oxford
instructed a Mr Churchill of Deddington near Banbury to defend
the action which it won.

On 30 August 1787 when the canal was opened to Northbrook,
15 miles south of Banbury, the *Alfred*—one of the Oxford's
boats—returned to Banbury amid acclamation of the different
parishes. The contractor and proprietors had breakfast on board
between 09.00 and 10.00 arriving Banbury 14.30.[9] Immediately
there was a general meeting at which it was resolved to open a
wharf at Enslow and another to be opened two weeks later at
Shipton, only 7 miles from Oxford.

The building of the canal was now making good progress and
in January 1788 the Oxford agreed to Simcock's proposal to take
the canal through Kidlington Green instead of Begbroke.
Shortly afterwards it requested Simcock and Weston to provide a
plan and estimate for taking the canal through land belonging to
St John's and Worcester colleges at Oxford. Their plan was
agreed, but the men were still finishing the canal to Hayfield Hutt
wharf a quarter mile from Oxford. The demand for coal in
Oxford brought by canal to this wharf compared with the previously more expensive 'Newcastle' brought up the Thames resulted in the company writing to Bedworth near Coventry asking
the miners to 'give the Boats to Oxford one day's preference in a

c

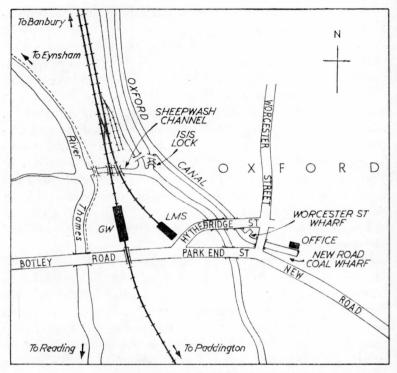

FIGURE 4.   Map of canal and river Thames at Oxford

week in loading, to others; as the call for coals at Oxford are
very great'.

In January 1789 whilst this work was in hand Simcock and
Weston were asked to prepare detailed plans for the final stage—
a new wharf near Hythe bridge in Oxford. The completed plans
were approved by a subsequent committee. The City Council
now became involved as it owned the land required but to make
things a little more difficult part had been leased to Worcester
college in 1777 for the sum of £33 which involved 'Quitrent' and
20p 'capon' money. Other parts had been leased to a Mr Osborne
and a Mr Johnson.[10]

Notwithstanding the fact that the legal transfer had not been completed the Oxford pressed ahead with finishing the canal and on 12 December was able to announce that the basin was now complete and on New Year's day the water would be let in. On 1 January 1790 the City of Oxford gave vent to its joyous feelings at the canal having finally reached its destination. With the bells from St Thomas church ringing out a welcome, a large fleet of boats bringing in over 200 tons of corn, coal and other goods made a triumphant entrance into the City basin headed by a boat with the band of the Oxford militia aboard playing under the Union Jack. The very next day *Jackson's Oxford Journal* carried an advertisement stating that Warwickshire coal was available for sale at 6½p per cwt.

The Birmingham & Fazeley was finished on 11 August 1789, and on 13 July 1790—the Tame aqueduct having been completed —the extension of the Coventry from Atherstone to Fazeley was opened at a cost of £30,000. The canal line from Manchester, Liverpool and the potteries was now complete, and immediately traffic began to pour forth from the Coventry down the line of the Oxford. The Hawkesbury toll collector, John Brown, was now taking so much money that he had to be provided with firearms to defend himself. By December he had to have an assistant who was paid 50p plus 10p lodging allowance per week. Brown only received 80p per week, though he was handling sums vastly in excess of this amount.

Arthur Young (1741–1820), a professional journalist, paints a varied picture of the state of the canal in 1791:

Shares in this canal for want of water, were down to £60 and even £50 . . . Reservoirs were exhausted, and the barges [narrow boats] last year nearly on dry land: they were very near the same spectacle this year, but by new exertions things are coming about again, steam engines are built or building, at the summit, three miles from Bransom [Braunston] and about twenty from Banbury, for throwing back the water wasted by passing the sluices; and, in consequence of this, shares are now got up to par.

At the end of January 1790 all those interested attended a site meeting in Oxford and agreed the area required for the terminals could be leased for a period of 40 years providing the Oxford company could assure them that all the ground including Jews Mount and Badcock's garden was required. Four days later Weston told them this was so. The completion of the legal formalities took much longer and were not, in fact, completed till June 1792 when the Oxford agreed to pay £320 for the site and £1 a year to both bailiffs and 26p to each of the 24 chamberlains.

Meanwhile in October 1791 the company decided that a warehouse should be erected at its Oxford terminal which was to become known as Worcester Street wharf. The building was to be 80ft long with a 30ft clear span. The foundations and pillars were to be of stone with arches of brick right up to the ceiling.

The cheapest form of labour in Oxford was the use of 'felons' kept in the Castle jail superintended by Mr Harris. He had already carried out two important navigational works for the Thames Commissioners, the building of Godstow and Osney locks, both in 1790 and it was to him that the Oxford turned for this project. The work on the basins and warehouses lasted well into 1795. To meet the bill of £3,045 the company had to borrow £2,500 at 5 per cent from the Old Bank (now Barclays) Oxford. Having met the requirements of the trade, an office was a necessity and one which would be near the terminal in the city. Accordingly in 1796 it agreed to purchase from Christ Church college and the city a portion of land near St Peter's Hall in New Inn Hall street. During the following year on this site it erected a Georgian residence known as Wyaston House, for £550 which, though superseded in 1829 by a fine Grecian office, remained in the Oxford's possession till 1878.

Following completion of the canal a general tightening up in all directions took place. The company found that they had no power to charge for traffic under 5cwt whereas on the other hand some unscrupulous carriers were charging above the laid-down scale of charges. In 1794 these items were covered by a further

Act which required the company to exhibit the laid-down scale of charges at each wharf. Also as an amendment to the original Act the company were empowered to mine clay, gravel or stone found within 1,000yd of the canal.

Peter Bignell of Banbury was the solicitor to the Oxford from the beginning; he also practised money scrivening, and went into banking about 1784 with two local mercers. But he continued his legal activities until his death in 1795. The Banbury bank of Bignell, Heydon and Wyatt was appointed local treasurer to the Oxford in 1787, on the death of Mr Calcot the previous holder of the post. The Oxford borrowed from many banks and this one was no exception. A sum of £654 was repaid in 1798 for money advanced towards the purchase of land for the canal. Child's of London whose banking origin dates back to 1649, with direct goldsmith antecedents back to 1586, were appointed bankers of the Oxford in 1783 and six years later the canal borrowed £2,000 from them at 5 per cent. This concern was succeeded by Harley, Cameron & Co, and upon their failure in 1797 Hammersley's of Pall Mall, London assumed the function.

The payment of dividends was still a headache for the Oxford till the trade grew appreciably. In July 1795 the payment of the modest half-yearly dividend of 2 per cent was held over till September because the lack of water in the canal, resulting from a long dry spell, had delayed the movement of boats. In fact there was no dividend at all between 1788 and 1790. Even then the financial troubles of the canal were not over, but local banking houses as will be seen from the following minutes were fortunately willing to tide them over the difficult situation.

The Committee appointed to examine the half year's account ending the 4th of this instant July having reported that the costs for new works etc. now carrying on will amount to £2,500 and this committee having taken into consideration the heavy charge already incurred by the company and placed to the current account since the expenditure of the loans to be great but remote advantage of their capital and understanding that Messrs. Fletcher and Parsons on application made to them for that purpose are willing to advance the said sum . . . and not to demand payment thereof before the company divide 5% without any circumstance previously occurring that may require their account to be closed, the committee to have liberty at all times to recall the sum or sums to be placed to the credit of the company by the said Fletcher and Parsons towards the discharge thereof until payment of the said sum . . . shall be demanded.[11]

James Barnes a native of Banbury, was the Oxford's engineer till 1794 and received a salary of £200 per annum. He left the Oxford canal in 1791 and joined the Grand Junction and carried out the initial survey in 1792 on behalf of the Marquis of Buckingham. When he died he was buried at Bodicote church, 1¾ miles south of Banbury, but his tablet on the wall only mentions that he was principal engineer of the Grand Junction.

Richard Tawney (1774–1832) was appointed agent and engineer for the Oxford on 12 November 1794 at a salary of £150 per annum, plus expenses. In 1799 he married a Warwickshire girl at Coleshill and about the same time moved from his Oxford address to Dunchurch Lodge, about 2½ miles south of Rugby.[12] With the company's improved financial position his salary had risen to £500 plus 'horse hire' and expenses by 1813. Besides working for the canal he bought the Banbury New Bank in 1819 in partnership with his brother Charles, and sold out in 1822. At the time of this purchase the two brothers owned £1,700 nominal shares in the canal plus £1,400 loaned to it at 5 per cent. His tablet on the north wall of Dunchurch church, though not so elaborate as Barnes's does give him greater credit: 'In Memory of Richard Tawney Esquire of Dunchurch Lodge who for many years with superior skill and integrity conducted the concerns of the Oxford Canal Company and by general decline ended an useful life at the age of LVIII on XXXI of January MDCCCXXXII.' Another appointment was that of a new wharfinger at Banbury in 1791. He was paid £1 per week with a house provided but had to find a surety of £300.

When all this was done, the Oxford were beset by two nagging

thoughts. Was it permitted by the 1769 Act to have its wharfs
within the city when it said 'to Oxford'? And who was to use
these wharfs—what about traders off the Thames who found the
Oxford's wharfs, which did not suffer from the river's floods and
droughts very much to their liking and yet only paid a very small
toll to the canal company?

Therefore towards the end of 1798 a Bill was promoted by the
Oxford which included clauses on these two aspects; the latter
invoked a storm of protest as it appeared to establish a monopoly
by authorising the purchase of existing wharfs or land for wharfs
and by excluding boats navigating the Thames from using these
wharfs, this being directed mainly against boats off the Thames
& Severn canal. The city council met and agreed to petition
against the Bill unless clauses objected to were withdrawn.[13]
Much correspondence appeared in *Jackson's Oxford Journal* and
the following extract from a notice printed on 12 January 1799
is perhaps instructive.

> The company has reason to expect security in its canal and wharfs
> and that coals coming from any other canal, and afterwards navi-
> gated on the Thames or Isis should not be admitted, because
> although the Oxford Company do not mean to prevent coals
> being brought to Oxford by canals communicating with the
> Thames or Isis, still conceive they have a clear right to prevent
> such coals coming on any part of their canal or being landed at
> their wharfs. The public wharfs belonging to the University and
> City are open for such coals and every canal company desirous of
> wharfs at Oxford may take the means to procure them as the
> Oxford Company has done . . . it was directed to be a free naviga-
> tion to prevent partiality and to allow of competition among
> traders in those coals which were to be procured by the canal;
> but it could not mean that coals should be admitted at the southern
> termination when it was necessary to make the canal ninety miles
> in length to bring them in from the north.

The Oxford bowed to the complaints and withdrew the clause,
but in fact they always refused permission to coal coming off the
Thames and the matter was never tested legally.

B.2

J.J.

LAND-TAX REGISTER-OFFICE,
N° 9, LINCOLN's-INN FIELDS.

I do hereby certify that the Contract under-mentioned hath been registered at my Office, by which the Estate specified therein hath been exonerated from the under-mentioned Land-Tax charged thereon, from the 25th Day of March, 1799.

COUNTY of *Oxford* - - - PARISH of *Bletchington* = *Hundred* = = *of Ploughley*

Name of the Contractor.	Amount of Land-Tax.	N° of the Registry.
The Proprietors of the Oxford Canal Company	£ s. d. - „ 15 „ 8¼	24242

Witness my Hand, this *10th* Day of *June 1799*

£. s. d.

William
Principal Register.

FIGURE 5.　Land-Tax Register Office form, 1799

The Bill now had an uneventful journey through Parliament and became an Act on 21 March 1799 by which the purchase of all buildings and lands were approved including those within the boundary of the city of Oxford.[14]

The company paid great attention to the facilities at Oxford and on a lesser scale the same could be said of the other wharfs along the line of the canal. An example was Enslow Bridge Wharf, 11 miles north of Oxford, which was on the turnpike road connecting Islip with Woodstock. Adjacent to the nearby bridge over the Cherwell was Enslow Mill, an unusual double one, mentioned in the *Domesday Book*.

The usual practice of the company was to offer a drawback on coal to enable business to be started up in the area in which the canal was being constructed even though it meant delivery by waggon. As early as 16 June 1787 a 1p drawback was being offered on coal to Enslow.

Business was quite often conducted in a pub and by May 1791 it was:

Ordered that the house at Enslow called Gibralter Inn now in the possession of Mr Henry Baker be let to him at the annual rent of £30 to commence from 1st January last upon condition that the Company's Wharfinger is accommodated in Mr Baker's House without any expense to them until a house is provided for him. Ordered that the meadow near the said Inn now in the possession of Mr Henry Baker be let to him at the annual rent of £10.

The wharfinger enjoyed the use of the inn till December 1793 when his own house was completed at a cost of £224.

Once the company had showed its willingness to assist the trade, advertisements would be placed in a local paper by one or more of the traders giving details of what was on offer:

15 October 1791. ENSLOW BRIDGE WHARF. Messrs Churchill and Baker beg leave to inform the Public in general, that they now sell coals of the best quality at the following prices viz

Wednesbury   15d per cwt
Badgley   14d per cwt
Bedworth   13d per cwt

also at their coal yard in Woodstock, at the same prices exclusive of 2d per cwt carriage, and will continue selling at the same rate at the above Wharf and Yard for fourteen days from the date hereof after which period the Coals must unavoidably be advanced unless the Canal in the interim became navigable.
NB Staffordshire Coak, at the said Wharf at 22½p per quarter.[15]

Though it took a little time the response in the end was quite gratifying and to show its appreciation the company raised the wharfinger's pay to £1 per week in 1795. The following toll receipts for Enslow clearly show the trend:

1793	£641
1794	£998
1795	£1,286
1796	£1,758

Coal was the principal traffic on the canal and every effort was made to boost the sales. To this end the company gave credit to traders at Oxford who stocked more than 500 tons of coal on the wharf. Even this measure was not enough to ensure that stocks were sufficient to see them over the period when the canal was closed due to ice.

The winter of 1795 had resulted in the canal being frozen over for ten weeks and as a result the price of coal had risen to 20p per cwt, but fell to 8½p as soon as it thawed sufficiently to allow the boats to get through. In January 1799 the company placed the following notice in *Jackson's Oxford Journal* in the hope that the public would purchase coal before the next winter:

> The public are requested to send for their Coals, as early as possible in the Season as may be convenient that the Stocks on the Wharf may be so kept up, as to prevent such a scarcity as was so felt by those persons who are unable to purchase more at a Time than their immediate wants require. The allowance made by the Company will not be continued after Michaelmas, without notice being given to the effect. Parishes purchasing coals for the use of their poor, will be allowed 5p per ton what is paid to normal individuals. This allowance will to be paid to all Parishes, however near to Oxford they may be situated.

Coal traffic for the year ended 6 July 1793 which passed from the Coventry to the Oxford was as follows:

Destination	Tons
Stretton	6,536
Hillmorton	13,487
Braunston	8,617
Cropredy	2,147
Banbury	8,389
Aynho	4,106
Heyford	731
Enslow	2,093
Oxford	9,787
TOTAL	55,893

This did not give the complete picture since coal from Wyken and Hawkesbury Hall collieries originated at the northern end of the Oxford. Indeed, the former constructed a basin in 1794 abutting on to the canal. Nevertheless, an indication of the relative importance of each wharf at this date is given.

Many of the narrow boats which conveyed coal in the southbound direction quite often found a back carriage. In addition there were a number of traders operating a set service, some of which travelled above a walking pace and were known as flyboats. In 1798 there were three scheduled carriers on the canal.[16] J. Couling operated a market type service between Banbury and Oxford serving all wharfs and any other point as requested. It is quite possible that he carried passengers too. This boat arrived at Banbury every Wednesday evening from Oxford for the market and by midday on Thursday it had been discharged and reloaded for the return journey to arrive in time for the Saturday market at Oxford. Thomas Sherratt's boats left Oxford every other day for Birmingham calling at Banbury, Braunston, Coventry, Nuneaton, Atherstone and Fazeley. When the canal was frozen he resorted to waggons to maintain a service. Lastly there was Joule's boats which set off twice a week from Oxford to the Potteries and Liverpool and Manchester.

As early as June 1788 advertisements were appearing in *Jackson's Oxford Journal* asking people to build boats 70ft × 7ft for the Oxford and no doubt arising from this a boat repair and building yard was established at Banbury in 1790. Mr Evans located this at the eastern end of Factory Street (previously known as Beck Lane) on the west bank of the canal above lift bridge number 164.

The boat dock was 90ft long, 16ft 6in wide, and from 4ft to 4ft 6in deep. Access was by stone and brick steps, one set at each end and a set in the middle of the west side. Boats entered the dock at the northern end. Once in the dock four timber baulks were dropped into place across the entrance and the wooden sluice door in the south-west corner was raised. The water level was lowered gradually enabling the boat to settle gently on the dock bed. It was then propped and secured before the remainder of the water was drained off. A gully ran the length of the dock along both sides and across the ends, enabling the small amount of water that escaped through the dam to run into the drain. This ensured a dry footing on the bed of the dock. The water from the dock was carried to a 6ft deep well between the dock and the canal via a stone drain, under the canal to another well in the towing path, and thence into the mill stream. The water was carried under the canal through an elm wood culvert measuring 9in × 9in internally, which almost certainly was laid before the canal was extended to Oxford. Although it was possible to build boats within the limited confines of the dock, this seldom happened. They were normally built and launched from the canal bank between the south end of the dock and the lift bridge.[17]

Even before the canal reached Oxford it was apparent that the number of boat movements in a dry season resulted in there being insufficient water in the 11 mile summit pound between Marston Doles lock and Claydon Top lock. This despite the fact that the pound had been dug over a foot deeper than all the rest and was coupled with the two reservoirs—Byfield and Clattercote—which fed it.

So in 1787 the Oxford agreed to purchase eighteen acres from Lord Spencer for £1,373.80. On this site immediately to the east of the tunnel and adjacent to the summit pound of the canal was built Wormleighton reservoir. Its twelve acres of water held 2,860,000 gallons.

This supply was sufficient for a few years, but trade was on the increase. Aynho wharf just south of Banbury was enlarged in 1791 and trade on to the Thames had just begun. The Oxford now realised that further supplies must be obtained quickly, so using the powers granted under the Act of 1786 by which it was allowed to use any water found within a thousand yards of the canal, it built a 900yd canal with one bridge which started between locks numbered 11 and 12 on the Napton flight. At the end a pumping engine was placed. From this point water was lifted into a brick channel, which after a distance of one mile, was discharged into the summit pound by Marston Doles lock. The land purchased for this branch cost £205.20. The company must have had a lot of trouble with the engine for in the first year the boiler had to be replaced at a cost of £70. Then two years later in 1796 a man was killed whilst attending to it and the Oxford made an ex gratia payment of £10 to his mother.

The company was fortunate in that all levels to the north of the summit pound descended to the Coventry. Although there was a 6in fall at this point, the Coventry found that this did not compensate for the 7ft drop at Atherstone top lock. Following a request from the Coventry in 1798 the Oxford agreed to raise all weirs on the then 26-mile pound between Hillmorton and Hawkesbury Junction so that any surplus water passed into the Coventry.

The 27½-mile extension of the canal from Banbury to Oxford had involved the construction of 28 locks each with a single top gate and bottom gate. Two of these—Aynho Weir lock and Shipton Weir lock—led off the river Cherwell and had a small fall of 8½in and 2ft 5in respectively. To compensate for the fall at the next locks—Somerton 12ft and Roundham 7ft 5in—they were made a diamond shape so that the volume of water used in locking through was equal to that required at the next lock.

Lift bridges are a great feature on this part of the canal. No less than 38 were originally provided. In addition there were 21 waggon bridges of stone and a further 20 of brick.

The exact cost of the extension to Oxford cannot be accurately determined because of other works carried out on the section between Hawkesbury Junction and Banbury; nevertheless the company had spent a further £102,000 since 1780.

The route of the canal to Oxford, being rural, presents a placid scene. It is never far from the Cherwell, and passes the delightful villages of Aynho, Somerton, Heyford, Kidlington and Wolvercote.

Five miles south of Banbury there was Adderbury wharf. Its wharf house was typical of the period when the canal was constructed. It consisted of an entrance hall, with living room and pantry off at the rear. The floors of these rooms were boarded, and covered a brick floored cellar which kept dry and was 'always useful'. Access to the cellar was obtained from steps down from the kitchen, or via a 'cellar light' outside, used for tipping coal. At the time this was unofficially obtained from any of the narrow boats going to Oxford each day for around 17p for a load of five or six cwt. In the living room there was a small fire grate and wall panelling to a height of about 4ft. In the kitchen, which was a stone and blue slate single storey building compared with the three storey brick and Stonesfield slate roof of the main block, there was a stone floor with a sink and pump. The pump was primed by a bucket of water out of the canal. There were bedrooms on the first and second floor, of which the second floor had two, one being entered from the other. Adjoining the kitchen was a store followed by a granary. The store contained the earth closet, there being no sanitation. Cooking was all done on the solid fuel grate and lighting was from paraffin lamps.[18]

CHAPTER 3

Trade onto the Thames

MUCH of the land taken for the canal near Oxford formed part of the Blenheim estates on which the grateful nation had built Blenheim Palace in recognition of the successful battle fought by John Churchill, Duke of Marlborough, against the French at Blenheim in 1704.

Since the fourth duke (George 1739–1817) was a large shareholder in the Oxford it was only natural he should think of ways to improve this source of income as a means of meeting the high cost of maintaining the palace at Woodstock.

Two and a half miles north of Oxford is the Wolvercote paper mill situated on a stream which runs parallel to the canal and is fed from the Thames just above King's weir between Eynsham and Godstow. It was purchased about 1720 by the duke and in 1782 leased to William Jackson, a prominent business man of Oxford. He was the proprietor of *Jackson's Oxford Journal*, a printer, bookseller, stationer and one of the founders of the Old Bank. Two years before taking the lease he had joined with the university and Archibald Hamilton in a partnership for conducting the Bible press.[1]

The duke, who had the lordship of Witney, knew that fuel was the greatest need in the upper Thames area as the woods had been greatly diminished and only about fifty tons of Newcastle coal, brought to the Pool of London by colliers and transhipped there to barges, reached this area each year. He realised there was a considerable marketing potential for Warwickshire coal brought down to this part of the country by the Oxford. He owned the land between the Oxford and the Wolvercote mill stream and as these two waterways were almost on a level, he envisaged that by making a cut between them traffic would avoid King's weir and thus not use the water of the mill he owned there, and at the same time not interrupt its working.

He must have mentioned his idea to the company as a 99-year lease at £6 per annum was granted to the Oxford for the land through which a 500yd cut could be made between its canal and the millstream.[2] Though the lease was never signed, apparently the company built the cut at a cost of £1,828.60. The opening date is unknown, but the first indication of its use is an advertisement in *Jackson's Oxford Journal* for 3 October 1789.

COAL WHARF AT HAYFIELDS HUTT

The Oxford Canal being finished and opened at the above wharf, within a ¼ mile of Oxford, the best coals, etc., are sold at the following prices:

Oakthorpe coals, equal in quality to	
Staffordshire	1s 5d per cwt
Warwickshire	1s 2½d per cwt
Staffordshire coke, per ton	£1 4s 9d

NB The above coals are delivered at the same prices upon the Wharf at Eynsham.

At the northern end of this cut there was a towing path bridge and the only other engineering feature was a lock. This was needed because the level of water in the canal was normally twelve inches above the Thames, however in times of flood the Thames could be as much as two feet above the canal. Robert Mylne, engineer, when he visited the site in 1802 reported to the Thames Commissioners that:

There is a single leaf gate, which shuts from the Thames, on an opening of 12ft 6in. It does not fit very close, and by a shutter, water can be taken into the canal. Besides this, there is a pound lock between this stop gate and the canal. The width is 13ft 2in at the lower gates; with 4ft 11in water on the lower sill and 5ft 3½in on the upper.

Plate 9 Claydon top lock, wharf and stables, 1974

Plate 10 Cropredy coal wharf and toll house 1974, showing the narrow point where boats were gauged

Plate 11 Banbury 1920. Starting in the foreground is lift-bridge 165, lock, canal company's wharf and warehouse, lift-bridge 164, Tooley's boat dock and Castle wharf

Plate 12 Grantham's wharf at Heyford 1792, which has long since disappeared

The reason for the Oxford refusing to sign the lease appears to have been that there was nothing in its Acts which mentioned a connection with the Thames at this point and this fact is confirmed by Andrew's and Dury's 1in map of the Country Round London produced in 1774 on which the intended line of the Oxford below Banbury is shown. The next step came in January 1792 when the cut was conveyed on trust to the Vice-Chancellor of the university and the Mayor of Oxford pending a settlement. After lengthy negotiations, a lease was signed in March 1798 whereby the duke's cut was leased to the company for a period of 200 years for an annual rent of £6 to the duke; later in November of the same year he was paid £150.9½p for rent and damage to his land over the previous nine years.

The original navigation of the Thames stretched from Cricklade in Gloucestershire to London, passing Lechlade, Eynsham, Oxford, Wallingford, Abingdon, Reading, Windsor and Staines. The latter point marked the upper limit of the Corporation of London's jurisdiction.

The remaining 120 miles of the river were controlled by Thames Commissioners, 600 in number, who formed local committees for each of the five districts into which the river was divided. Each committee had its own engineer, but all reported to the annual meeting of the Commissioners, who, acting for separate districts, were too often unacquainted with the interests of the whole, whilst many never attended meetings at all. There was no surveyor or engineer for the river as a whole.

In view of this strange management structure it is not surprising that the navigation of the Thames suffered numerous defects. Even so efforts were gradually being made to bring it up to the standard required by the carriers.

One other result of the cutting of a direct navigation between the canal and the upper Thames was the fact that the Thames Commissioners for the Oxford–Cricklade district did not receive any increased tolls at their Godstow lock situated between

D

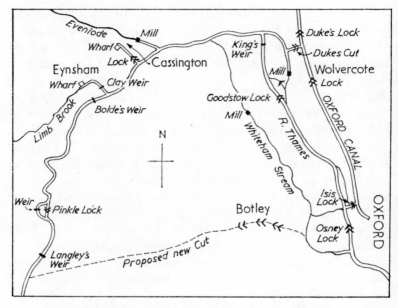

FIGURE 6.   Map of Thames, Oxford–Eynsham, 1802

Oxford and King's weir. Mylne saw this and in his report of 1791
recommended:

> that a weir be also erected at the Mouth of the Wolvercote Stream,
> with a pair of Gates ten feet wide to open upwards . . . in order
> to admit the passage of such boats as may pass by the new [Duke's]
> cut from the Oxford Canal into the Thames, on paying adequate
> toll . . . being informed that boats passed this way with coals to a
> considerable amount.

No action was taken but Mylne did not give up. In 1802 when
making yet a further report to the Thames Commissioners he
stated:

> At the mouth of the Wolvercote stream, which passes, to the
> left, and northwards, there is good water of five to four feet. It
> would be well and proper to establish two jetties at this place,

having a sufficient width between; and, from the piles at the head
of these jetties, a strong chain may be stretched across, by a
windlass, and raised up to the surface of the water, occasionally,
to collect tolls of all boats passing from and out of the Oxford
Canal.

The Commissioners, however, were not to be moved, so they
lost any chance they might have had of obtaining revenue on
narrow boats whose journey started or finished short of Pinkhill
lock, the next one up the river owned by them. Conversely they
had to ensure that the river was properly dredged to meet the
depth requirements of a fully laden narrow boat. It was a somewhat ridiculous situation no doubt reflecting the type of management mentioned earlier, though perhaps their thoughts were
centred on yet another large potential revenue earner—the
Thames & Severn canal.

This canal was the realisation of a much mooted project among
London and Bristol merchants in the reign of Charles II, but it
had to wait till 1783 before its Act was finally obtained. This
canal, unlike the Oxford, was built to take boats up to $12\frac{1}{4}$ft in
width and throughout its history water was a serious problem
since it seeped away in large quantities through limestone found
in the summit pound. It joined the Thames at Lechlade in
Gloucestershire and was opened on 17 November 1789, estab-
lishing a communication with Wales, Bristol, Gloucester and
Shrewsbury and the canals of Staffordshire, Warwickshire and
Oxfordshire.[3]

Therefore in the space of a few months the Thames Commissioners for the Oxford–Cricklade district had to deal with prob-
lems arising from two major canals suddenly joining their system.

The places between Pinkhill lock and Godstow lock benefiting
from the duke's cut were Eynsham and Cassington. Both also
served Witney and Burford, in consequence they could be
considered to be in competition. The wharf at the former was
owned by the Oxford for 101 years and that at the latter for only
seven years.

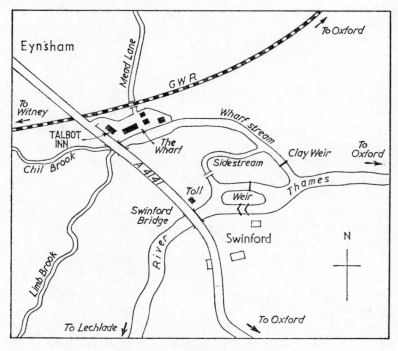

FIGURE 7.   Map of Eynsham, 1928

Eynsham is situated some six miles by road from Oxford and
five miles from Witney, the home of the famous blanket industry.
A Benedictine Abbey was founded at Eynsham in 1005 and a
lease of 1302 mentions a Hythe or wharf, situated at the con-
fluence of the Chil and Limb brooks where the stream had been
widened to make a landing place for barges, and deepened to
form a navigable channel down to the Thames half a mile away.[4]
Cargoes included hay, straw, malt, grain, and timber; in 1310 and
1331 stone from Taynton quarry near Burford was loaded here
for the building of Merton college, Oxford.[5]

The advertisement mentioned earlier gives the first indication
when traffic arrived off the Oxford. The company gradually took

steps to build up the trade. In May 1790 it allowed traffic to pass at a special rate which was a reduction equal to 5p per ton per mile. By next April James Lord, a coal merchant, was asking for the privilege of payment by account which was agreed to in July.

In January 1792 the company decided it must have a permanent representative at the wharf, so it appointed a wharfinger at 60p per week with house and in the following year the company carried out general repairs to the house and wharf.

The wharf stream was usually too shallow to float a fully-laden boat right up to the wharf. To overcome this difficulty a flash-lock or swing gate known as Clay weir was built a little way up stream from its junction with the Thames below Bolde's (Eynsham) weir then in the ownership of the Earl of Abingdon who also owned the adjacent toll-bridge known as Swinford.[6] After a boat had passed through the gate it was closed, and the paddles or rimers were slotted into position against it to hold back the water. A side stream controlled by a sluice permitted water from the Thames above Bolde's weir to pass into the wharf stream; this, together with the natural flow, raised the level and allowed boats to proceed up to the wharf. A charge of 5p per boat was made for the operation of Clay weir, perhaps performed by the keeper of Bolde's weir.[7]

From Eynsham coal moved by road to Witney, Burford and beyond. These places also received Welsh, Forest of Dean and Staffordshire coal via the Thames & Severn, unloaded at Lechlade, Radcot and Newbridge wharfs on the Thames. To ensure that Eynsham received the lion's share of the traffic the Oxford offered traders in 1794 a rebate of 5p per ton on all loads which passed through the turnpike gate at Witney providing a certificate was signed by the keeper of the gate and a declaration made by the trader on the back of the certificate to whom the coal was sold. This offset to some extent the road carrier's charge of 20p per ton to which probably had to be added food and drink for the carters. In 1797 the company paid £184 in rebates which indicates a tonnage of 3,680. Incidentally whilst coal sold at £1.40

per ton, salt fetched no less than £23.50 per ton. Any advantage was short lived as the Thames & Severn adopted the same line of action as evidenced by the following advertisement which appeared in *Jackson's Oxford Journal* on 30 November 1799:

BOUNTY ON COALS

To Burford, Wantage, Witney and Faringdon. The Thames and Severn Canal Company hereby give notice, that they will allow a bounty of 10p per ton until Lady Day next on all Newport and Bilston coals sold at their wharf, at Lechlade, upon the purchaser producing a certificate that the same tons have been conveyed to Burford, Wantage or Witney and a bounty of 7½p upon same coals having been conveyed to Faringdon.

In 1800 James Lord sold his business including boats to Joseph Bowerman, who quickly improved trade.[8] In the first five months he despatched over 150 tons of coal by waggon to Burford. During the same year also the Oxford leased the wharf from a Mr Jammett for £60 a year. This gave it the control necessary to enforce its policy of not allowing coals off any other canal to be landed at its wharfs. Consequently, when any of the Eynsham traders brought coal via the Thames & Severn it had to be unloaded on to one of the adjoining meadows.

Cassington mill has stood beside the river Evenlode, which joins the Thames between Eynsham and the duke's cut, since before the time of the Norman Conquest, and in later years it formed part of the Blenheim estates. The branch canal to Cassington which passes by the mill is first mentioned in the Act of 1800 which confirmed the Cassington Closure award.[9]

A Canal there made by and belonging to the said Duke of Marlborough for the conveyance of goods to a certain wharf there belonging to the said Duke of Marlborough . . . Allotment herein awarded to the Duke of Marlborough for his freehold estate being the wharf and towing path of the new canal.

The accompanying map showed that the canal as then built only connected the pool below the mill to the new Cassington-

Eynsham Road, but by 1802 the canal was completed through to the Thames on a straight line from the wharf. The only engineering work was an entrance lock on which Robert Mylne, engineer, in his report to the Thames Commissioners in 1802 stated as follows:

> There is a good and substantial Pound Lock constructed of these dimensions. It is 112ft long Gate to Gate; and 14ft 10in wide. It pens 4ft 11in, from the River level to that on the cut, which is the same as the mill head at Cassington town . . . The width of the cut, on the surface, is only thirty feet; and the length about six furlongs.

So this short canal was able to receive boats off the Thames & Severn and even though owned by one of the Oxford's chief shareholders it nevertheless competed for a number of years to a certain extent with that company's facilities at Eynsham.

Henry Baker was the wharfinger. He had served previously at Enslow on the Oxford. The duke agreed to Baker building a small house, the timber and freestone for which were to be supplied by the duke after he had agreed the plan and estimate for the work. Together with the miller, John Patrick, Baker agreed in the same year to erect two lime kilns and pay 1p per ton on all stones landed, and 1¼p per ton on all coals and other articles landed or despatched on the understanding that the duke endeavour to procure a licence for selling ale there for the accommodation of the trade.[10] This he did, but it cost the partners £10 each in sureties before the authorities would allow the Barge Inn to be opened. Baker lasted till 1821 when he became a debtor owing the Oxford £12.

William Langham, his successor, was probably the most successful tenant of the wharf and the buildings he occupied must have been considered of great importance in Cassington since in 1823 he paid £2 in Poor rates, as compared with £1.50 paid by the millowner.

To gauge the relative importance of Cassington as compared with Eynsham, the following figures of tolls paid to the Oxford by the principal users of each wharf during the year 1824 are instructive: Eynsham—£1,753; Cassington—£795.

There had been changes at Wolvercote mill too; in 1793 John Swann succeeded William Jackson. Not only did he set about modernising the business but he extended the premises in 1804 by purchasing Eynsham mill situated on the river Evenlode above Cassington mill. In 1811 a coal-fired steam engine, requiring 100 tons of coal a week, was introduced at Wolvercote mill for making paper, water power being retained for breaking and pulping rags.[11] The coal was supplied from the Midlands and therefore passed down the Oxford through the duke's cut and down to the mill.

The following figures for traffic which traversed the whole of the Oxford and passed through the duke's cut in 1824 clearly show its importance as a connecting link: North to South— 5,488 tons; South to North—470 tons. No doubt if figures were available for local traffic movements they would show a substantial increase on these.

For a short period the duke's cut formed the only link between the Thames and the Oxford, until the company made its own connection in Oxford; therefore traffic going down river had to pass through King's weir, Godstow lock and Medley weir before reaching that city. But what a route—complaints about its navigational qualities were legion—so much so that in 1793 they formed the subject of a Commons Committee of Enquiry.

The Thames Commissioners opened a new lock at Godstow in July 1790, but this apparently left a lot to be desired since T. Court, a bargemaster of Oxford, said that the sill was laid too high, and the lock cut was of insufficient depth, so that it was worse than before and more expensive.[12]

Samuel Simcock, engineer to the Oxford, examined the situation in 1791 and reported to the Duke of Marlborough, who as a riparian owner was entitled to be a Thames Commissioner, on the section above Godstow suggesting that gates and sluices be affixed to Godstow bridge to increase the depth of water over the shallows.[13] The suggestion was implemented. Strangely enough the duke made no charge for boats passing through King's weir. From the Oxford's angle, though, the more difficult it was for wide boats off the Thames & Severn to reach Oxford, the better.

Simcock also examined the section below Godstow and suggested improvements costing the staggering amount for those days of £936.50. The towing path by Port Meadow had been washed away in many places and bargemen were using the farmer's fields opposite instead.[14]

In 1624, the Oxford–Burcot Commission was formed to improve the navigation of the river Thames over the fourteen miles between Oxford and Culham. This enterprising body built pound locks, which were among the earliest in England, at Iffley, Sandford (by the paper mill) and Abingdon. Later the Thames Commissioners were empowered to take over the whole of the river and the Oxford–Burcot Commission who represented the Oxford University and city interests then known as the commissioners of the sewers. On 13 August 1789 they advised the city council that the Thames Commissioners wished to buy out their interests for £600 and it was agreed that this sum should be accepted.

The Oxford had formed a junction with the Thames in Oxford in March 1790, probably with some form of movable weir, but from the canal company's angle it was not really very satisfactory since every time a boat passed through it all the water was let out of the basins.

The matter was raised at a local committee meeting in September 1792 and they put forward the recommendation that a pound lock should be built.

A chain of questions was sparked off by this suggestion. Firstl should the Oxford trade on the river Thames, and if so should barges be used; and if goods were to be transhipped into them from narrow boats would it not be sensible for this to be done at the company's wharf? To this set of questions the answer was—yes! May 1793 saw the ordering of a barge for £71 suitable for conveying goods down into the tidal waters of London, and at the same time following a request from the Oxford the Thames Commissioners agreed to dredge the Sheepwash channel which links the Thames above Osney bridge, Oxford with the Thames backwater above Hythe bridge. Daniel Harris, the keeper of the felons in Oxford castle, was asked in August to construct Isis lock which he completed in 1796 at a cost of £1,979. And thus the Oxford started trading off its canal in Thames barges. How well this plan succeeded is not known, but in 1800 Worcester Street Bridge was widened to allow Thames barges into New Road Coal Basin. All this transhipment work cost money; 25p was normally allowed for shifting twenty tons of coal. The canal company really put its heart into it and ordered barges for the trade as follows: 1795 (1), 1800 (1), 1801 (3) and 1802 (6), making quite a large fleet.

There was one big snag for boats moving to and from the new wide lock (Isis)—there was no towing path bridge over the Sheepwash, so the horses had to be taken down the canal to Hythe bridge, along the Botley Road to Osney bridge and back up the Thames towpath.

The building of Isis lock provided an opportunity for narrow boats journeying on the Thames to avoid the navigational difficulties between Medley and King's weir by using the Oxford canal, the duke's cut and the Wolvercote Mill stream. The Company made a nominal charge for this movement and the Yarnton Meadsmen, survivors of medieval strip farming, made their usual charge for boats being taken along that part of the Wolvercote Mill stream between duke's cut and King's weir.[15] There was another snag similar to that at Oxford—no towing path bridge over the Wolvercote Mill stream. So after tying up the boat at the beginning of the Wolvercote Mill stream, man and horse had to return to the canal, down the towing path to Wolvercote bridge, through the village, over Godstow bridge and up the river towpath to pick up the boat. This walk of three miles was unavoidable in the absence of some means of ferrying the horse over the river at King's. The same problem existed for boats destined for Wolvercote Paper Mill, where it was the practice to tie up the boat at the end of duke's cut, take the horse back to the stables at Duke's lock, then shaft the boat backwards with the current down the stream to the mill.[16]

In 1793 the company introduced a scale of drawbacks for coal moving down river, the most generous relating to large cargoes passing Caversham lock, Reading; in 1794 these were adjusted and the most favourable rate was brought back to Benson lock. But it soon discovered, as it had at Eynsham, that the best way to promote trade was to have representatives in the area and, if possible, wharves also.

Accordingly in 1795 it purchased a wharf at Reading on the river Kennet. This navigation up to Newbury was partly owned by Francis Page, one of the canal company's shareholders, who was also on the committee of the Kennet & Avon canal then being constructed to link Bristol with London. Whilst the building of this canal would provide a route for merchandise traffic off the Oxford destined for Bristol, it would also connect with the Somersetshire Coal canal and thus inject further competition into the coal trade at Reading, which then obtained its supplies either from inland sources via the Thames & Severn or Oxford, or coastwise up the Thames from London. Happily for those already in the field supplies from the Somerset coalfields were not available in quantity till the completion of the Kennet & Avon in 1810. In the meantime £1,231 was spent on repairing the wharf and then, in 1800, it was leased to an agent for 99 years.

Sometimes private negotiation did not produce the desired result, so that it was then necessary to advertise for facilities as instanced by the following which appeared in *Jackson's Oxford Journal* on 4 May 1799.

To Wharf Owners and Landowners on the River Thames
Wanted to rent for a term of years a Wharf and a Warehouse for the accommodation of general trade, either at Shillingford or

Wallingford; or land conveniently situated within three miles of these places, whereon a Wharf and a Warehouse may be made. Apply at the Canal Office, Oxford.

Charles Toovey of Reading soon contacted the Oxford and as a result he leased to it a wharf on the north side of the bridge at Wallingford for eighty years from 29 September 1799 for an annual charge of £30.

The only other wharf on the Thames in which the company had a direct interest was at Abingdon, nine miles down river from Oxford.

At this point the Wilts & Berks canal joined the Thames. This narrow canal had obtained its Act in 1795 and ran via Swindon to join the Kennet & Avon which in turn provided access to the Somerset coalfield. This canal, like the Kennet & Avon, was not completed till September 1810.

The first mention of the coal trade at Abingdon is in 1799 when the Thames & Severn was advertising Tenby coals for sale at £2.62½ per ton and Newport coals for £2 per ton.[17] Both of these would have been conveyed coastwise from South Wales ports to Framilode on the river Severn before starting their journey by canal over the Cotswolds to the Thames. Next year the Oxford started competition in earnest by offering 'a Premium of 5p per ton on coals taken from the Abingdon wharf to places 10 miles away and 10p if carried to places 14 miles away'. In 1801 it bought the Abingdon wharf from Thomas Fletcher for £500.

The Thames & Severn perserved with its business for quite a while, but in July 1806 it announced that its wharf was for sale. No doubt the state of the Thames between Oxford and Lechlade was the root cause. For the river over this section had numerous shallows and only a few locks. Water in the main was held back by a number of 'flash' weirs which, when opened, allowed the water to rush through taking the barge with it. But if the vessel was going up river it was a hard task to pull the barge through against the surging water. Not surprisingly the traders who used this part of the waterway made many complaints about its condition. So much so that in January 1802 the Commissioners felt it necessary to ask an eminent engineer to examine the river.

Robert Mylne carried out this survey and during the course of his investigation he was asked to report on a proposal from the members of the upper Thames district for a new canal starting about 2½ miles west of Eynsham below Bablock Hythe ferry through the village of Botley to a point below Osney lock in Oxford, so as to reduce the mileage by the Thames between these points.

In his report he recommended that a 66ft wide canal 3 miles long should be constructed from above Langley weir to a point below Botley mill on a branch stream which led into the Thames below Osney lock, a saving of over 7 miles.[18] The canal was to be level to Botley, then falling 18ft 6in through four locks each costing £1,200 with sloping sides, and out via the tail of the Botley mill stream. The estimated cost was £15,020, which included three road bridges, a towing path and a cutting over 30ft deep. The scheme was approved and as the ground required for this canal was owned by the Earl of Abingdon, the Commissioners wrote a letter to the Rev Dr Weston, the receiver of rents for the earl's estates, seeking his approval for the project. In the meanwhile advertisements were placed in the Gloucester, Oxford, Reading and London papers to raise the capital and a surveyor was asked to make a detailed survey and plan for the proposed canal.

However, the latter reported in June that the length was over 3½ miles and the Commissioners realised that by their Act of 1788 they were not allowed to make any canal or divert the Thames for any distance in excess of 3 miles.[19] In view of its use by narrow boats off the Oxford, they would still have to maintain the present navigation particularly to Eynsham and at the same time lose tolls at their Pinkhill, Godstow and Osney locks. The Oxford stood to lose revenue on the traffic which used its canal between duke's cut and Isis lock. On the other hand the Thames & Severn would reap the benefit.

Notwithstanding the known limitations set by the Act, the Thames Commissioners sought counsel's opinion which unfortunately confirmed the position and they therefore asked Dr Weston for details of compensation which the earl and his tenants would expect if the canal was built. The reply was not immediately forthcoming, but when it did come in 1805 the earl stated that 'the canal would so completely cut up my estate, that much as I wish to promote the public advantage; I cannot consent to a measure that will so entirely ruin a principal part of my property and consequently feel myself having to oppose it.'[20] Whether his reply was clouded by the fact that he owned Eynsham (Bolde's) weir on which he would lose money by the construction of this canal is a matter for conjecture.

In the end the Commissioners had to abandon the idea. Nevertheless they did say that they would not oppose any private concern seeking permission to make this canal. So died a project which might have affected the Oxford's revenue.

However the Thames & Severn was quite determined that its waterway should not suffer because connecting systems were not up to its standard. If improvements could not be effected in the Oxford area then it must consider alternatives elsewhere such as joining the Thames further down river and this in fact is what it eventually achieved.

One year after the Wilts & Berks was opened throughout, the Thames & Severn agreed jointly with it to assist a proposal known as the Severn Junction canal which envisaged the two waterways being connected by a short canal between Swindon on the Wilts & Berks and Latton near Cricklade on the Thames & Severn not far from the source of the Thames. This proposal in fact was linked to a much larger scheme for a canal called the Western Junction from the Wilts & Berks at Abingdon to the Grand Junction near Marsworth which envisaged making use of the latter's proposed branch to Aylesbury. The petition for the Bill was introduced into the House of Commons on 1 February 1811 and immediately the opposition started to prepare its case.

The Oxford could see Staffordshire coal reaching Abingdon and points below there on the Thames in competition with its own from Warwickshire, with traffic for London, which passed up the Oxford and down the Grand Junction, being diverted over the new route. Oxford University was the first to petition against the Bill closely followed by the City council and then the canal company itself. The Thames Commissioners in association with towns on the Thames also petitioned against the Bill. Such was the strength of the opposition that after much debate the Bill was defeated at its second reading on 25 February by a majority of ten.

Great was the rejoicing. So much so that on 11 July the Oxford assembly considered it important enough to give the chairman, the Rev David Durell, £2,000 partly 'as an acknowledgement of the permanent and substantial benefit derived from his late unwearied assiduity in defending and supporting the interests of the canal'.

But that was not the end of the saga. In October the Wilts & Berks announced in the local papers that a new survey for the Severn Junction had been authorised and that a meeting would be convened in the Goddard Arms at Swindon on 6 December to discuss the matter. As this was now not connected with any other proposal the opposition was found to be much less than previously when the House of Commons received the petition for the Bill on 18 December. In March the Oxford petitioned against, but this time it did not have enough support, so the Bill for the canal, whose title had now been changed to the North Wilts, received the Royal Assent on 2 July 1813.[21] This 9 mile long canal, with twelve locks, a small aqueduct over the upper Thames, and a short tunnel was opened on 2 April 1819. Despite this set-back the Oxford still managed to carry 18,000 tons of coal down the Thames for Abingdon and other points below, in 1827.

CHAPTER 4

All Waterways lead to London

THE Oxford no doubt felt well pleased that its canal had joined the Thames at a point where the navigation was not too bad. Generally speaking in 1790 the state of the river was in stark contrast to that pertaining at the present day. Shoals and shallows abounded and below Maidenhead there were no locks at all, so that it was hardly surprising as soon as traders had tried this through route by water from the Midlands to London that agitation arose for a more direct canal which would not only be shorter and therefore quicker but what was of more importance —reliable.[1]

During 1791 several people suggested possible solutions and eventually the Oxford decided that something had to be done. It discussed the matter on 11 January 1792 when it was said 'a scheme or schemes hath or have been in contemplation to form lines' of communication to London and other places by a Junction 'with the Oxford canal at Braunston or Aynho'. If either of these ideas ever came to fruition the company felt it would stand to lose a lot of money since London traffic would cease to pass over the whole length of its canal. Action had to be taken and taken quickly, so engineers Simcock and Weston were despatched immediately to explore the country between Thrupp (six miles north of Oxford) and London to see if a canal was practicable between these points.

The Times correspondent was soon on the trail, for when writing only two days later he said of navigational possibilities:

Plate 13 Heyford wharf 1973, looking towards Banbury

Plate 14 Summer at Baker's lock, Enslow, 1955

Plate 15 Towing-path bridge 217 erected in 1909 over the River Cherwell. Baker's lock can just be seen on the right

Plate 16 Shipton weir cottage erected in 1851 beside the diamond-shaped lock which gives access to the river Cherwell

'The River Colne, a Canal from Oxford to Edgware [London], the junction of the Dee and Severn through the lakes at Ellesmere, are all now under consideration.' Soon it was apparent that there were two distinct schemes under consideration: (a) the Hampton Gay or London & Western canal by certain members of the Oxford Canal Company, and (b) the Braunston or Grand Junction canal by a separate organisation. The plan produced by Weston provided for a narrow canal of 61 miles in length. It was to leave the river Cherwell just north of Thrupp and proceed for 16 miles on one level passing Islip and Thame, then a rise of 261ft with a branch to Aylesbury followed by a fall of 474ft across Hounslow Heath and into the Thames above Isleworth.

The papers were soon full of comments about the merits and progress of the rival schemes.

The Times on 13 April after commenting favourably on the Grand Junction project said:

> That another scheme is in agitation for an extension of the Oxford Canal to London, from a place called Thrupp within six miles of Oxford, but as that will be near 30 miles greater distance (than the proposed Braunston Canal) . . . and as it will very materially injure the Thames Navigation, by running nearly parallel with it the greater part of its course, it is expected that the Promoters (who are a few leading Proprietors in the Oxford Canal) will, upon more mature deliberation, abandon that scheme, especially as there is a large body of the Proprietors themselves more desirous of the extension taking place immediately from Braunston.

Soon the Thames & Severn heard of the London & Western project and as it had been languishing under the bad state of the Thames decided to ask Robert Mylne, an engineer, in May to consider how best to make a canal from the Thames above Oxford to join the new gateway, but nothing further in this direction transpired.[2]

Though the London & Western was not being supported by the Oxford there was nevertheless a very close tie up as is evidenced by two separate advertisements that appeared in the same

E

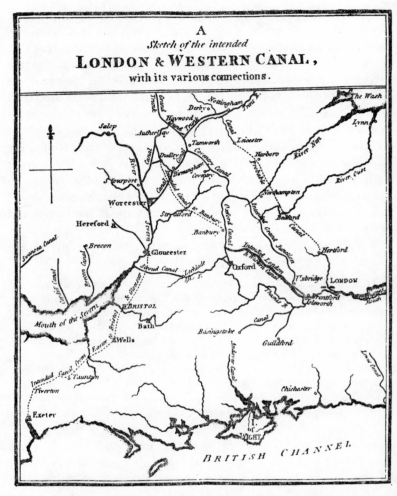

FIGURE 8. Map of intended London & Western canal, 1792

edition of *Jackson's Oxford Journal* which states the proprietors would meet to discuss their respective canals in the same place at the same time.[3]

It seems the Oxford committee was playing a double game. On one hand it allowed certain of its members to back a scheme favourable to those taking traffic to London down the Thames from westward of Oxford, thus securing additional revenue over that part of its canal which had adequate water supplies. At the same time it let another group propose a canal from the base of the hills below Napton locks through an area which was not served by canals and would therefore generate traffic over and above the London traffic already passing down the line of the canal to Oxford. If the improved system captured the imagination of the merchants, then the overall increase in traffic should outweigh the anticipated loss over the summit level, leading to a net increase in revenue coupled with a saving of water.

A look at Fig 8 will show that the two proposed canals ran quite close together from the top of the Chiltern hills near Marsworth down to the Thames. Quite obviously Parliament, not to mention the land owners affected, would find this difficult to justify. A gentleman who signed himself simply 'Amicus' suggested in a letter to *Jackson's Oxford Journal* on 5 May that the two canals should be united and operate under the title of the 'Union Bucks Canal'.

To this idea was added yet another by the Marquis of Buckingham who suggested that the canal should start at Hayfield Hutt Oxford in the Parish of St Giles and proceed through Marston, Elsfield and Woodeaton to Islip where it would take up the line of the canal as already planned.[4]

The original plan and the two alternatives were printed on 1 September and placed before the General Assembly of the Oxford at Banbury a week later, when it was decided 'to back all three horses' by inserting notices in local papers to conform with Parliamentary Standing Orders so that all three proposals could be considered for inclusion in a Bill.

On the same date as the meeting the Grand Junction had given notice in the papers of its intention to apply for an Act and the Oxford's appeared only one week later on 15 September.

But what of the Union Bucks idea which on the face of it appeared sensible, for as long ago as 28 July it had been decided to hold a meeting with the Grand Junction to discuss the proposition. This eventually took place at Buckingham on 22 October when the Hampton Gay delegation put forward the following proposals: (1) Equal participation of expense and profit upon both undertakings. (2) Each company to cut to the junction, and have the profits on its own section; from the junction, equal expense and participation. (3) As 2, but each company to take the separate tonnage of all vessels navigated from its own particular section.[5]

Evidently the Grand Junction was pretty confident as it dismissed all three proposals and instead suggested that it make the entire canal from the junction at Marsworth to Brentford, and allow Hampton Gay vessels to navigate upon payment of a 'moderate' (!) tonnage rate. But what was meant by 'moderate', the Hampton Gay soon learnt on 27 October when it was informed that the Grand Junction would allow a 10 per cent drawback on the tonnage of all vessels to and from the Hampton Gay Canal between the junction and the Thames. The Hampton Gay in turn, rejected this suggestion and countered with the idea that it make the canal to the Thames and allow Grand Junction vessels to pay the same rates as Hampton Gay vessels between the proposed junction at Marsworth and Uxbridge. Alas, compromise was not to be achieved, so what might have been a worthwhile alteration was lost for ever.

For an indication of the actual support at this time for the two schemes the following purchase prices for shares are perhaps a useful indication: ten Grand Junction shares fetched £451.50; five Hampton Gay shares fetched £63.00.[6]

Notwithstanding the setback over compromise with the Grand Junction coupled with the apparent public lack of support, the Oxford held a meeting at Woodstock on 1 December and agreed by a big majority to support the Hampton Gay scheme and oppose the Grand Junction's.[7]

The Thames Commissioners, who perhaps stood to lose more than anybody if the Hampton Gay was built, convened a meeting on 19 December and agreed to appoint a committee to oppose the Bill.[8] Their action resulted in petitions against it from towns on the Thames such as Henley, Reading, Wallingford and Windsor.

The Grand Junction introduced its Bill into the House of Commons on 20 December 1792 and eleven days later it received a formal first reading. The time was now opportune for the Oxford to submit its petition against the Bill and this it did on 20 January 1793. It claimed that prior to 1786 income did not equal expenses, furthermore only 1 per cent dividend had been paid in 1789. In 1790 this was raised to $1\frac{1}{2}$ per cent but in 1791 it was still only 2 per cent. The company had also borrowed over £130,000 to complete the canal, so was naturally most anxious to ensure that its financial position was safeguarded.

At a meeting in Woodstock on 21 November the Oxford proprietors decided by a big majority to back the Hampton Gay by every means in their power and likewise to oppose the Grand Junction. On 17 January 1793 both the Oxford and Hampton Gay proprietors petitioned the Court of Common Council at the Guildhall, London, against the Grand Junction scheme and this petition was referred to the navigational committee.[9]

At long last on 11 February the Bill for the Hampton Gay was presented with a supporting petition by the Duke of Marlborough. Samuel Weston, the engineer who had done the plans for the canal, was examined by the House on 20 February being supported by Hugh Henshall, Brindley's brother-in-law who had served as engineer to the Trent & Mersey and also by Samuel Simcock engineer to the Oxford.

So far so good, but although petitions in support of the Bill had been received from Amersham, Aylesbury, Chalfont St Peter, Great and Little Missenden, Isleworth, Oxford, Uxbridge and Wendover, those against from the Thames valley commanded greater influence, so much so that on 8 March the House of Commons decided that the matter should be deferred for six months. Nothing further took place, and the last rites of the Hampton Gay project were on 18 January 1795 when a notice appeared in *Jackson's Oxford Journal* to the effect that the committee were only able to pay back 6p out of every £ originally subscribed.

Part of this scheme was promoted in 1806, when the section from Shipton to Aylesbury appeared in an advertisement in November stating an application would be made in the next session of Parliament for a Bill to make this canal. The Oxford decided to oppose it; the Grand Junction had in fact already considered this scheme at their meeting on 18 September where it became apparent that the main reason for its resurrection was tied up with an attempt to force that company to build the branch from Marsworth to Aylesbury which was in their Act of 1794.[10] Nothing further transpired on this projected canal from the Oxford.

The Oxford, however, was still intent upon safeguarding its revenue as far as possible. To this end it succeeded in having inserted in the Grand Junction Bill, bar (compensation) tolls of 14p per ton on coal and 21½p on all other traffic except lime and limestone. Furthermore, if its receipts did not exceed £5,000 per annum once the Grand Junction was opened from Braunston to Old Stratford then it was to be paid the shortfall and when the canal was finished, or after 1 January 1804, the Grand Junction was to make up the difference if the receipts did not exceed £10,000. Happily for the Grand Junction the tolls taken at Oxford alone exceeded these figures.

Work on cutting the Grand Junction began in the early part of May including the great tunnels at Braunston and Blisworth. On 21 June 1796 the first 8½ miles south through Braunston tunnel to Weedon were opened. At this time the canal for the 9 miles on to Blisworth wharf was well advanced—heavy earthworks were involved—and completion was hoped for in August.

In fact it was not till a month later that this stretch was completed and then a water shortage prevented the company from filling it. Boats probably started working over the 17½ miles to Blisworth in October.[11] As a result of numerous difficulties with the tunnel at Blisworth the canal was not completed till 25 March 1805.

James Barnes who had been responsible for the building of the Oxford below Banbury, was the Grand Junction's resident engineer being paid a fee of £1.05 per day and 52½p per day expenses. When he left the canal he became a partner in Austin's brewery at Banbury.[12]

Up to June 1805 the water from the Grand Junction's locks at Braunston emptied out into the Oxford, but from that date the Grand Junction brought into service an engine which pumped back the water to the Grand Junction's summit level. This had been made possible by two small reservoirs placed alongside the canal between the bottom lock and the junction with the Oxford. The reservoirs were supplied through a special paddle at the bottom lock, which discharged all the lockage water into them apart from the last six inches which went into the final stretch of the canal and hence into the Oxford.[13]

The takings at Braunston toll office together with tonnage show the change from a country wharf, increasing steadily as the Grand Junction is built and then after completion a rapid rise which I think exceeded the wildest dreams of the Oxford company.

Year	Tolls (£)	Tonnage
1793	966	953
1794	1,011	1,045
1795	894	1,026
1796	2,156	517
1797	3,908	4,053
1798	5,307	4,246
1799	6,406	5,913
1800	6,604	6,840
1801	5,898	5,906

Year	Tolls (£)	Tonnage
1802	6,680	6,426
1803	8,422	9,979
1804	12,648	11,197
1805	17,299	14,978
1806	19,040	18,495

The Grand Junction's toll office was established in 1796 when they appointed James Cherry as clerk with a salary of £90 per annum.

Ever since 14 July 1790 the Oxford had been connected with the Birmingham canal following the completion of the aqueduct over the river Tame on the Birmingham & Fazeley. Braunston, at the passing of the Grand Junction's Act, was situated about seventy-six miles by water from Birmingham.

Warwick, whose 'King Maker's' castle overlooks the river Avon, was not connected to the canal system and having seen the benefits others derived from this cheap form of transport thought that it should be connected with Birmingham, a city of rapid industrial expansion coupled with an excellent coalfield, some of whose seams were 30ft thick. This idea was born in 1792 and culminated in the Warwick & Birmingham Canal Act, 1793.

Whilst all this was going on the people promoting the Warwick & Birmingham thought it would be a good idea to continue it on to connect with both the Oxford and the Grand Junction. The project was particularly attractive as the journey would be much shorter and therefore tolls should be saved, not to mention time.

In June 1793 William Felkin, engineer to the Warwick & Birmingham, together with James Sheriff, Charles Handley and Samuel Bull, engineer to the Birmingham, surveyed the area in between and finally decided upon a line from Warwick to Braunston to connect with the Grand Junction. Also there was to be a branch to join the Oxford on their summit pound at Fenny Compton.[14]

The Oxford once again asked for high compensation terms

especially as Birmingham traffic would cease to pass over its northern section. The Warwick & Braunston sought a meeting with the Oxford committee and even travelled to Oxford to meet them when they were in session, but were kept waiting and in the end went home without seeing them.

This was now the canal mania period when waterways were being projected in all directions, therefore it is not surprising to find that another company was also promoting a line to join the Oxford at Fenny Compton. This was the Stratford-upon-Avon canal authorised in March 1793 with a line starting from King's Norton on the Worcester & Birmingham to Stratford-upon-Avon. It estimated 40,000 tons of coal from Dudley and 10,000 tons of other traffic would pass over this branch in one year and as the anticipated cost of construction was only £80,000 it felt justified in offering the Oxford compensation terms which included a clause to the effect that the Oxford was not to be connected by a branch from the Warwick & Braunston. Unhappily for it the Oxford had just lost its Hampton Gay battle and therefore was looking for greater financial safeguards—£5,000 against loss of trade was suggested. The Warwick & Braunston did not fare much better—£4,000 was the figure asked of it.

The Stratford issued Parliamentary notices for the Fenny Compton extension, but the proposal went no further, presumably because the authorising of the canals through Warwick had made it too speculative.

The Warwick & Braunston Bill was introduced into the House of Commons in January 1794 and quickly drew a petition from the Coventry complaining about the anticipated loss of receipts on Birmingham traffic which naturally would be diverted over the shorter route. Another opponent was the Stratford-upon-Avon which was obviously still considering an extension to its own line as its petition intimated that the Warwick & Braunston had not given the matter proper consideration and furthermore new ideas might be forthcoming if the Bill was delayed; this no doubt referred to its Fenny Compton scheme.

The Stratford-upon-Avon's friend, the Worcester & Birmingham, stated in its petition that the route chosen would provide excessive lockage—a fact which years later was to provide an expensive item for the Grand Union. The Bill eventually passed both Houses and received the Royal Assent on 28 March 1794.

The reason why the Oxford did not petition against the Bill was plain to see from the Act as, once again, they had secured high bar (compensation) tolls. Fourteen pence per ton was to be paid on all coal moving off the Warwick & Braunston into the Oxford. Lime and limestone, which was then in great demand as a fertiliser, was to pay a toll of only 6p per ton. All other traffic, unless passing to and from the Coventry, had to pay the maximum bar toll of 21½p per ton. The Oxford had, therefore, by virtue of its cross-roads position, inserted bar tolls which in years to come were to provide more than ample reward! Not only had it taken care of the change in movement to and from other canals; it had also covered the possible reduction in traffic to its local wharf at Willoughby near Braunston. A clause in the Act stated that if coal from the Oxford dealt with at that point did not exceed 324 tons in a year, then the Warwick & Braunston was to pay 14p for each ton short. Lastly a rather cruel requirement so far as the Warwick & Braunston was concerned, as its canal descended from the Oxford down to Warwick, was the provision of a stop-lock at the junction with the Oxford to ensure that the level of water in the Warwick & Braunston was kept 6in above the Oxford's.

It was not till the following year that work started on cutting the new canal. Hardly had things got under way when Charles Handley thought of a brilliant way to save £50,000 by shortening the line and eliminating an 800yd long tunnel. The Warwick & Braunston approved the idea in September and on 14 October wrote to the Oxford seeking its assent to the junction being at Napton instead of Braunston, with of course suitable adjustments to the financial points in its original Act including the deletion of the Willoughby wharf clause. Following its agreement the

Warwick & Braunston drafted a bill which was presented to Parliament on 5 February 1796.

There were only two petitions against the Bill—from the Grand Junction and the Ashby, both of which were of no real consequence—and the Bill soon passed all its stages and received the Royal Assent on 14 May. Henceforth the Warwick & Braunston was known as the Warwick & Napton.

Because the junction at Napton was 5 miles west of Braunston the bar tolls were, in the main, increased. The 14p for coal off the Warwick & Napton was raised to 16½p. Although lime and limestone which provided the main fertiliser for farmers remained unaltered at 6p per ton all other traffic rose from 21½p to 26p per ton. A couple of new variations were also included. Coal off the Warwick & Napton which found its way on to the Grand Junction was only to pay 14p, but much to the delight of the Grand Junction it was to get 2½p per ton on all traffic except lime and limestone which moved between the Warwick & Napton and points on the Oxford south of Napton.

The supply of water had still not been resolved; immediately after the passing of the Act the Warwick & Napton wrote to the Oxford asking if water could be supplied whilst it was cutting the section between Napton and Leamington.[15] How it was to be supplied after that is pure conjecture! Anyway the Oxford took a realistic view and declined the request because it felt it would result in a shortage during a dry season on the summit pound.

The Warwick & Napton was now in a serious quandary and the only way out of its dilemma was to reach an agreement with the Oxford.

In 1797 therefore it drew up the following list of proposals which were laid before the Oxford committee:[16]

1 That the Warwick & Napton could at its own expense enlarge the reservoir in the parish of Boddington in the county of Northampton to contain at least a further 15,000 6ft locks of water, supplying it with flood water.

2 That the Warwick & Napton was to pay the expense of making

the reservoir but also the expense of maintaining it and the feeder into the Oxford.

3 That 12,000 6ft locks of water annually were to be released out of the reservoir into the summit pound of the Oxford if required.

4 That the quantity of water run from the reservoir into the Oxford was to be measured by a servant of the Oxford jointly with a person appointed by the Warwick & Napton.

5 That the Warwick & Napton was to pay all reasonable expenses involved in measuring the water.

6 That in consideration of the Warwick & Napton providing water for the summit pound of the Oxford, that company was to give up the right to the 6in higher level required by the Act of Parliament and also allow boats to pass the stop lock without impediment.

The proposals were well received by the Oxford, but no action appears to have been taken.

In April 1798 the Warwick & Napton submitted revised proposals to the Oxford by which it was to pay £500 pa for water providing the 6in requirement was lifted and that there was no interruption at the stop-lock. The Oxford declined this proposal but kindly suggested it would be willing to consider alternatives.

Eventually on 13 June 1798 an agreement was signed by which the Warwick & Napton was to pay the Oxford 10p for each boat passing to or from its canal. So that the Oxford could count the number of boats passing and ensure the top lock was kept in proper repair it was to appoint a keeper at Calcutt who was to be paid by the Warwick & Napton.[17]

The first account for water submitted on 4 January 1800 was for £26; presumably trading had started before the completion of the canal on 19 March.

As in the case of the Grand Junction, trade soon increased as will be seen from the Napton toll office figures given below:

Year	Tolls (£)	Tonnage
1799	841	13
1800	4,925	3,103
1801	7,431	5,819
1802	8,213	8,555
1803	12,379	9,709

One other canal, though not joined directly to the Oxford, was to provide a large quantity of traffic in due course, particularly coal. This was the Ashby de la Zouch canal, which was to be built from Ashby Wolds, not far from Burton on Trent, by way of Market Bosworth and Hinckley, to join the Coventry near Griff only 2½ miles from the start of the Oxford at Hawkesbury Junction.

In 1792 notice was given of an intended Bill which was quickly followed by a suggestion that it might be extended on the other side of Ashby Wolds to the Trent at Burton, in which case it would have linked the Coventry and Oxford, and through them the Thames with the Trent. There were, however, formidable difficulties. It was claimed that the cost would be at least double the £46,396 estimated by the engineer Robert Whitworth, since for a canal of 31 miles that worked out at merely £1,500 a mile, whereas the Coventry and Oxford had cost £3,000 a mile. Both these canals were already well supplied with coal from other districts and it was felt to be doubtful whether a sufficient demand could be built up for coal from the pits at Oakthorpe and Measham to make such an expenditure remunerative. Moreover the majority of the landowners on the proposed line were reported to be hostile, and were making preparations for an opposition meeting.[18] The project was therefore dropped for some years.

The Ashby, when resurrected in 1792, immediately became the subject of the usual battle between rival groups of landowners. The first Bill was wrecked in 1793 on a technicality concerning Standing Orders.

Nothing daunted, the promoters of the plan immediately prepared to renew the application for a Bill in the following session, and this was passed on 9 May 1794.

Nevertheless the pessimist who had prophesied in a letter a few months earlier that it would be many a long year before subscribers saw any return on their money proved to be only too correct. This wide canal was built without a single lock except from the stop-lock at Marston where it now joined the Coventry. It was, however, not completed until 19 April 1804.[19]

A local trade in coal and Ticknall lime was opened up to the wharves at Bosworth, Sutton Cheney and Hinckley, but the larger anticipations of the projectors was unrealised. The criticism advanced in 1782, when the canal was first mooted, that the coal mines which it served, competing with those of Warwickshire and Staffordshire, could not expect to find sufficient markets to make it a profitable concern, seems to have been well founded. However one traffic did transfer immediately to this canal when it was opened. This was traffic from London conveyed by Pickfords for Leicester. Previously the boats had terminated at Brownsover wharf near Rugby from which point it was conveyed by road. In January 1802 the Ashby asked whether they would consider Hinckley, Market Bosworth or Sutton Cheney. Pickfords in their reply requested toll reductions so a tripartite meeting was held at which the following drawbacks were agreed: Oxford—5p per ton; Coventry—2p per ton; Ashby—1½p per ton. The transfer was effected as soon as the Ashby was opened and the drawbacks were not withdrawn till 6 October 1810.

The bylaws of the Oxford published in 1808 contained no less than thirty-three clauses which covered a multitude of sins and J. Dunsford, the clerk to the company, required all the staff to see that they were obeyed and if not they were to report the facts to the local magistrate and only in cases of doubt or difficulty was the felony to be reported to him or Mr Tawney.[20]

These clauses covered the usual items, such as name of owner on boat, provision of gauges on sides determining tonnage in boat, stating where contents were destined and correct operation of locks. In the latter connection, to avoid waste of water, boats within 200yd of a lock with the water level right for their entrance were to be given preference. In later years to avoid dispute, metal plates with the letters 'DIS' were set up at the stated distance from the locks. No boats were to be moved or any work done at the wharves on Sundays, Christmas Day or Good Friday. In such manner the company ensured that the biblical teaching 'on the seventh day thou shalt rest' was respected. Although the Factory Acts regarding the age of employment were still in the future, nevertheless, the Oxford insisted that the person leading the horse must be aged ten or upwards, likewise the steerer had to be eighteen or over. The preponderance of loaded boats were moving in the Oxford direction and it was therefore right that they should have preference over boats moving northwards irrespective of whether they were bound for the Coventry, Grand Junction or Warwick & Napton. 'Fly boats' which travelled faster with the aid of an additional horse and using a lighter boat were to be given preference. These boats were specially licensed and by 1827, 113 boats using the Oxford exercised this privilege.

In the early days of the railways it was said that noises from engines would upset horses and other animals, but this idea was not new since one clause reads 'that no person or persons navigating or being with or belonging to any boat navigating upon the canal, shall use any horn or noisy instrument by which cattle near to the canal may be frightened or disturbed'.

Pity the poor boatmen who had to seek permission from the company's wharfinger before he was allowed to make a fire or even sleep on his boat when moored at any of the company's wharves. In line with the age, penalties were quite stiff, amounting in some cases to as much as five pounds.

CHAPTER 5

Modernisation

THE Oxford's financial position now really began to show the results of its endeavours and the shareholders reaped part of the benefit, though it must be admitted a substantial proportion came from bar-tolls.

Year	Tonnage	Revenue (£)	Dividend (%)
1801	37,929	37,996	8
1802	40,061	40,791	10
1803	44,371	46,022	11
1804	49,272	48,901	12
1805	53,353	56,503	13
1806	59,992	57,832	16
1807	57,914	60,162	19½
1808	65,698	71,677	22
1809	78,253	79,438	25

The levels for dividends seem even better when we remember that at this time income tax was only 10p in £1.

Traffic movement was considerable as can be seen from the breakdown of the tonnages which passed between the Coventry and the Oxford at Hawkesbury Junction during the six months ending 31 August 1807. (See table on following page).

Even assuming a maximum payload of 30 tons per narrow boat, which is very unlikely, this represents 2,472 loaded journeys.

The Warwick & Napton soon found that the water agreement was not meeting its full requirement, so in 1803 it asked its

Plate 17 Duke's junction showing towing path bridge 232 with Duke's stop lock in distance, 1973

Plate 18 Duke's cut looking towards the river Thames in 1973 showing the Oxford–Witney (A40) bridge which was erected in 1933

Plate 19 Wolvercote paper mill in 1955 with coal from a pair of narrow boats being unloaded by machinery

Plate 20 Lift bridge 238, erected in 1831, by St Edmund's School Oxford, 1948

Harecastle coal	4,674 tons	Merchandise	28,003 tons
Wednesbury coal	13,824 ,,	Limestone	5,608 ,,
Warwickshire coal	12,599 ,,	Salt	2,597 ,,
		Crates	3,862 ,,
TOTAL COAL	31,097		
		TOTAL	40,010

GRAND TOTAL 71,107 tons

engineer, Charles Handley, to represent to the engineer of the
Oxford that great loss was being experienced by its boats having
to take turns on the Napton locks for want of an adequate water
supply.[1]

In December 1805 the Warwick & Napton decided to raise a
sum of £12,000 to procure a better supply of water for its canal.
Four months later the committee resolved that Charles Mills of
Barford, Warwickshire, be requested to wait upon Lord Spencer
and endeavour to obtain his agreement to the making of a reservoir at Boddington. Mills had his interview with Lord Spencer
and found him agreeable to the proposition but wishful to be
certain that the Oxford had the necessary Parliamentary powers
to construct a reservoir for the benefit of itself as well as the
Warwick & Napton. The Oxford, of course, had no such powers.
The Warwick & Napton then had another idea. In December
1806 they proposed a reservoir for 14,000 locks at Ashby St
Ledgers just north of Braunston tunnel in Northamptonshire, but
the Oxford opposed the plan and the Grand Junction imposed
so many conditions that it was dropped in February 1807.[2] Therefore shortly afterwards the Warwick & Napton and Oxford
committees agreed a draft Bill and it eventually came before
Parliament for approval. It had a relatively uneventful passage
and received the Royal Assent on 25 July.

Work started in 1808 and eventually it was completed by the
Oxford in 1811 at a total cost of £21,601.04 of which the Warwick & Napton paid £20,958.09. The difference represented legal
fees. This reservoir had a 33ft dam and fed the summit pound of

F

the Oxford just north of Claydon Top lock. Following its construction the Oxford ceased regular pumping at Napton and also
to ask the Warwick & Napton for 10p per boat passing Calcutt
locks.[3]

Trade was continually on the increase and in due course
demand for water again exceeded the supply. On 31 October 1832
the Oxford had to inform the Warwick & Napton that the reservoir at Boddington was empty. Action soon followed; by 21
January 1833 plans and sections for enlarging the reservoir were
laid before the Warwick & Napton committee who resolved that:

> The same appears to this committee clear and satisfactory, and
> that the addition to the Boddington reservoir will produce the
> necessary supply advantageous to both parties, and are approved
> of by this committee; and who are of the opinion that the works
> should be proceeded with at the earliest convenience, in order to
> prevent a similar alarm to that of last season, and to remove every
> apprehension of want of an ample supply of water to carry on the
> trade—and to defeat the interested statements put forth that the
> trade of the country cannot be carried on by water communication
> and canals.[4]

Such was the importance attached to this work that the
Warwick & Birmingham agreed to contribute £1,500 towards
the cost. The Oxford naturally was just as interested in the en-
largement and soon agreed the proposals which were carried out
quickly at a cost of £4,723.84. It was the practice for the Oxford
to carry out any maintenance as required from time to time and
charge the Warwick & Napton a proportion of the cost. For
instance on 6 February 1840 the Warwick & Napton paid
£111.80 for the half yearly expenses at Boddington.

Ever since the Grand Junction had got its Act it had pressed
the Oxford to widen and straighten the canal between Braunston
and Hawkesbury to take boats 14ft wide. William Praed, MP, the
chairman of the Grand Junction, reported on 22 January 1794
that the shortening of the Oxford between its canal and the
Coventry by 9½ miles would cost £32,089.41 and to widen the

rest would cost £16,408.80. As the Oxford's financial position at this time was still uncertain, nothing was done; a pity as the shortening when done in later years was to cost it dearly.

The Oxford, however, was not insensible to requests from traders and following repeated complaints about the shallowness of the canal it used a primitive excavator in 1814 to deepen the section between Hillmorton and Hawkesbury by one foot which saved boats carrying a full payload no less than four hours. This move was not enough to placate the neighbouring canals who convened a meeting attended by the Bridgewater, Trent & Mersey, Birmingham, Coventry and Grand Junction at which several resolutions were passed concerning the urgent need to shorten and widen the northern part of the Oxford. Once again it decided, in its wisdom, to take no action.

Years slipped by with no action until the Oxford was brought up with a sharp jolt by an advertisement in *Aris's Birmingham Gazette* of 12 November 1827 for a new wide canal designed by engineer Thomas Telford (1757–1834), known as the London & Birmingham Junction. This proposal envisaged a really magnificent waterway—a towing path on both sides and paired wide locks. It was to leave the long summit pound of the Stratford-upon-Avon near the feeder from the Earlswood reservoir, cross the Warwick & Birmingham at the top of the Knowle locks and join the Grand Junction at Braunston, thus avoiding the Oxford altogether.

One week later the Oxford committee met and considered the project 'highly injurious to the interests of the company'. Quite obviously the Oxford now had to make a positive move so, on 13 February 1828, it appointed Sir Marc Isambard Brunel, a naturalised Frenchman married to an English woman, to make a survey for shortening the northern part of its canal. His report was accepted and his fee of £512 quickly paid. Charles Vignoles was then called in and produced detailed plans on 8 October 1828, which envisaged the canal being shortened by $13\frac{5}{8}$ miles.

This was achieved by a number of new 'cuts' including em-

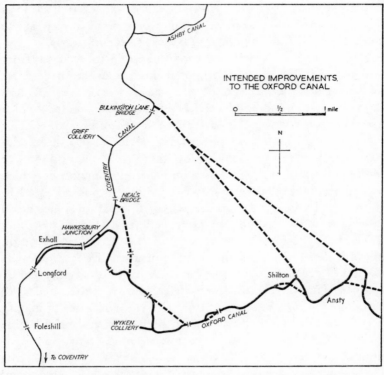

FIGURE 9. Map of new junctions proposed between the Coventry and
Oxford, 1828

bankments with larger aqueducts enabling the canal to cross the
sides of the valleys further downstream than the original line,
which had faithfully followed the contours, deep cuttings and a
new tunnel at Newbold near Rugby. Certain parts of the original
line were to be retained either as feeders or to serve an existing
wharf, such as:

Stretton	2 furlongs	Newbold Lime	
Fennis Field	4 „	Works	1 mile 1 furlong
Rugby	1¾ „	Cosford	1 mile 2¼ furlongs
Clifton Mill	3½ „		

A good example was the new cut of ¾ mile at Braunston which necessitated a cutting for nearly a quarter of a mile and a massive embankment for about the same distance together with a three arch brick aqueduct at a height of 45ft over the river Leam. This saved 3¼ miles of the old route, eliminated four bridges and the small 33yd tunnel at Wolfhampcote for an estimated cost of £17,000.

As soon as Vignoles's detailed plans became known the London & Birmingham Junction altered its proposed route from a point just east of Coventry to join the Oxford just west of Stretton by bridge 27. This canal was to have seventeen locks descending from the Stratford-upon-Avon and one rising at the junction with the Oxford, which, even allowing for the three Hillmorton locks on the Oxford, compared favourably with the 77 locks on the route into and out of the Avon valley at Warwick that were such a handicap to this canal route.

Then various Clerks of the Peace had deposited with them in November 1828 the maps etc showing the alterations intended, the prelude to the Oxford's petition for a Bill which was placed before Parliament on 16 February, and contained Vignoles's estimate for shortening the canal.

Earthworks including puddling	£74,059
Masonry	29,569
Towing path and fence	4,458
Land	11,802
Contingencies	11,989
	£131,877

Could the Oxford really afford this level of capital expenditure? The answer was definitely yes. In 1828 toll receipts had been £89,336 from which the shareholders received a dividend of 32 per cent plus a further 2 per cent bonus. Furthermore during the period of reconstruction this level of dividend was maintained.

Surprisingly enough the petitions in support of the Bill, with one exception from the manufacturers of earthenware in Stafford-shire, came from villages along the canal. Those against the Bill included merchants and traders in Birmingham, the Warwick & Napton, Charles Lord, the Bishop of Oxford, the turnpike trustees of the Old Stratford–Dunchurch road and the inhabitants of Braunston.

Numerous traders were called before the House of Commons examining committee and the comments made by Frederick Fleet, agent to Austin's brewery of Banbury, sheds light on the delays encountered when less than full boat loads were sent by water. Beer in casks sent to an inn at Warwick took 48 hours because it had to be transhipped at Braunston whereas when sent by road throughout it only took 8 hours.[5] Since he was against the Bill because of the bar-toll at Napton it is possible that canal rates were not really competitive in this instance.

The Bill soon passed both Houses and received the Royal Assent on 14 May 1829. The resultant Act showed the Oxford had bowed to some of the pressure to reduce bar-tolls whilst at the same time keeping other charges up.

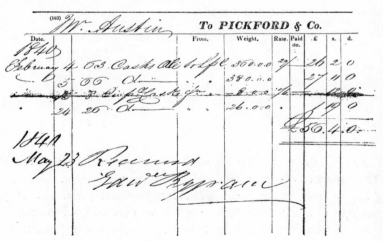

FIGURE 10. Pickford & Co's Bill, 1840

Despite the fact that the canal was to be shortened, rates of ½p per ton for coal and ¼p per ton for all other traffic were still to be charged on the original mileage as a form of compensation for the expense involved.

The compensation tolls off the Warwick & Napton were reduced to the following levels:

Coal and grain	7½p per ton
Steelwork, iron and sand	6p „ „
Lime and limestone	1½p „ „
All other traffic	15p „ „

Generally speaking all other bar-tolls were held at their previous figure, but coal off the Grand Union, which had connected Leicester and the north to the Grand Junction in 1814, was to pay only 7½p per ton.

As mentioned earlier the London & Birmingham Junction had moved the point where it proposed to join the Oxford nearer to Coventry. After making sure the Oxford's Bill had passed it prepared its own Bill, which was introduced into the House of Commons on 19 February 1830. On 4 March it passed Standing Orders. However, all was not well, as several gentlemen who had been mentioned in the subscription list petitioned the House to the effect that they had not been asked to subscribe to the scheme and furthermore they were not in agreement with it.

A special sub-committee therefore was asked to examine this matter and report back which they did on 5 April as follows:

that a great part of the said subscription had been proved to represent needy and indigent persons, of inferior state in life, deeply engaged in bubble companies and gambling transactions, and unable to pay the sums affixed to their names in the said list. No knowledge or consent for other shareholders some of whom were principal members of the Stock Exchange . . .

The House was quite startled by this revelation and for some time was in a quandary as to what course of action to take. In the end it was decided to call the promoting solicitor—Thomas Eyre Lee of Birmingham—to the Bar of the House.

He duly attended on 21 May and was reprimanded by the Speaker as follows:

> The House, after lengthened and mature consideration of the case in which you are involved and having given every attention to the petition you have presented, have come to the conclusion that the offence which you committed is of a grave and serious nature, as affecting the dignity and character of this House, and of the most dangerous consequences to the property of individuals who may be concerned in the passing of Private Bills. It has been proved to the conviction of the House, that the Subscription List which you deposited, was false and fictitious in itself: and that you, though warned as to the suspicious character of the said list, did, nevertheless, as agent for the Bill, attest its truth . . .

And there for the moment this project rested. At the end of 1833 a group of promoters, it seems with the backing of Lord Dudley and other Staffordshire coal and ironmasters who opposed the restrictive toll agreements then in force between the Coventry and Warwick canals, planned the London & Birmingham canal. The line, which was surveyed by James Green, was to run from the Stratford-upon-Avon canal to pass through Banbury, Buckingham, cross the Grand Junction near Tring, and run to St Albans and Highgate, where a branch was to link up with the Regent's canal. In all, it was to be 113 miles long with forty-eight locks, with a further twenty-two locks on the Regent's canal branch. From the Stratford canal there were to be nineteen locks and then a level pound of over 70 miles to St Albans. But nearly 10 miles of tunnelling would be needed as well as an enormous aqueduct over the Avon valley, whilst the cost was estimated at about £3,000,000.[6] A prospectus issued in March 1836 envisaged an elaborate set up. Where tunnelling was necessary twin tunnels each with a towing path were to be made, the sides of the canal were to be walled and a double towing path was to be provided throughout. Naturally the Grand Junction opposed the whole idea and in 1837 compromise proposals were put forward for a canal starting from Lapworth on the Stratford which crossed the

Warwick & Napton at Kingswood and again at Southam, dived under the Oxford in a tunnel near Wormleighton, and after passing Towcester joining the Grand Junction at Stoke Bruerne.[7] Not only were rival canal companies disenchanted with the scheme, but the promoters found it impossible to raise the capital needed, which was scarcely surprising as the current vogue was then investment in railways. There was a final meeting in Cubitt's London office on March 1838, but thereafter the plan for a new canal seems to have died a natural death.

Meanwhile work was proceeding on shortening the canal and eventually between 4 and 13 May 1834 the stoppage took place to bring into use the improved line. In fact, just over eleven miles were constructed; certain alterations although authorised by Parliament were never carried out and in consequence the total route mileage saving was only just over eleven miles. The cost of these alterations as detailed below amounted to £167,172.27 which compares favourably with the estimate given earlier.

1	Land 142 acres	£15,431.79
2	Compensation and damage	3,455.47½
3	Railways	6,845.93½
4	Waggons and barrows	2,514.48½
5	Boats	5,206.05
6	Workshops	498.38
7	Cast iron posts for paths and temporary barriers	258.29½
8	Iron for aqueducts	7,201.23½
9	Iron for guards	1,344.29
10	Bricks	12,456.07
11	Brickwork	6,323.02½
12	Stone and stonework	9,401.67½
13	Carpenters work	2,192.14
14	Timber	4,664.34½
15	Smiths work	2,763.35
16	Lime and sand	2,171.43½
17	Cutting, banking and puddling	68,652.48½
18	Towing path and walling	15,723.72½
19	Carriage of materials	8,176.53½
20	Day work	7,689.95½

21	Fencing	1,740.19
22	Rents	175.25
23	Incidental expenses	927.84½
24	Supervision and surveying	6,840.80½

TOTAL   £171,448.76½

To this figure should be added £3,000 for the cost of obtaining the Act and against this there was a credit of £7,276.49½ in respect of materials and land sold after the completion of the works up to June 1843.[8]

The results of these alterations produced an interesting selection of bridges on the canal, including 155 brick bridges, 10 archways, 8 iron towing path bridges, 5 wooden footbridges, 22 stone bridges, 42 draw bridges, 3 wood towing path bridges, making a total of 245 bridges.

The new 204½yd tunnel at Newbold was a really magnificent structure built to dimensions capable of dealing with a considerable increase in traffic. It is a lofty 14ft 4in from water level to the crown of the arch and its width of 24ft leaves room for a 3ft 8in towpath on each side of the 14ft 8in wide water channel. Although there has only ever been a single towpath at the approaches to the tunnel it would have been possible to use both sides within it as the portals were constructed with long ramps on each side making them each into an unusually large roving bridge. Unfortunately 83yd of the brickwork soon started spalling and had to be cased with a blue brick in 1847.

The Grand Junction benefited most from the improvement. Though traffic over the Oxford increased as well, the revenue only went up slightly due to reduced bar-tolls as will be seen from the following Oxford tonnage receipts: 1835—£72,465; 1836—£81,523; 1837—£86,176; 1838—£86,638.

In Chapter 1 mention is made of the several attempts to improve the junction at Hawkesbury between the Coventry and Oxford. Vignoles when carrying out his survey for shortening the northern section had included in his plans three schemes for reducing the distance on the London–Manchester route between Bulkington on the Coventry and Coombe on the Oxford as under:

(a) Bulkington–Ansty—length 2¾ miles with ¾ mile tunnel plus two short cuts of 1 mile and ½ mile.

(b) Bulkington–Shilton—length 3 miles with a 1 mile tunnel plus two short cuts each of ½ mile.

(c) Neals Bridge–Wyken Wide—length 1 mile.

These proposals were discussed by the Coventry at a special general meeting on 29 January 1829, but no decision was made. The last named scheme was incorporated in the Bill by the Oxford but following petitions against it from the Coventry and also Francis Parrott of Hawkesbury Hall, through whose coalfields the new cut would have been constructed, the Oxford agreed in the committee stage to withdraw this item on 27 April. All was not lost as the Coventry could see the value to through traffic of an improvement, so following a committee meeting on 10 September it agreed to approach the Oxford regarding the Bulkington–Ansty scheme. Its delegates saw the Oxford and eventually reported back on 22 April 1830 to the effect that they had been unsuccessful in prevailing upon the Oxford to unite with them upon terms which in their opinion were fair and equitable to both parties. Further efforts were made by the Coventry in 1834, but again these were of no avail.

In 1835 Frederick Wood, engineer to the Oxford, produced a plan for a twelve chain cut immediately to the north of the present junction which would have cut out the very difficult turn at Hawkesbury Junction and reduced the distance between Rugby and Nuneaton by 2 miles. This was discussed by the Coventry on 29 September and apparently approved, but the negotiations over the division of payment once again failed and the project lapsed. The Coventry did what it could on its own; it erected a new bridge for £630 at Hawkesbury in 1837 as well as a towing path bridge over the Oxford for £20 and thereafter maintained the junction at their own expense.

Although during the shortening of the northern section the lowest of the three locks at Hillmorton had been repositioned no action was taken as part of this programme to widen or duplicate them. The increase in traffic after 1834 resulted in delays to boats awaiting their turn to pass through this set of locks. At last the Oxford decided to undertake the duplication of these three locks which was completed on 25 August 1840. No doubt if they had possessed a little more foresight the new locks would have been wide enough to pass two narrow boats and thus ease the working for a pair of boats when steam haulage was brought into more general use on the canals. These locks, which had a sill clearance of 4ft 6in and were fitted with iron gates, had proved very difficult to build due to running sand. This no doubt accounted for their very high cost of £4,200.[9]

The Oxford were very mindful of the number of boats which would need to pass through these locks and therefore conducted tests to ascertain just how quickly a boat could be locked through even allowing for the use of the paddle at the centre of the lock which enabled water to pass into the adjacent chamber and so save part of each lockful. The timing from the test came out as low as 1min 20sec.

Installed also was an engine to raise water 18ft 10¼in, this being the aggregate lift of the three locks. The engine was sited behind the Hillmorton workshops 2½ chains from the canal. Water from this canal was spilled over into a channel which ran to the north of the three locks before discharging into the top pound. This 22hp lifting engine had a 26in diameter cylinder, a working barrel of 24in, a stroke of 6ft 6in, which made twelve strokes per minute thereby raising $4\frac{21}{30}$ locks of water per hour which necessitated the use of 1½cwt of coal.[10] In recent years this was replaced by a 32 bhk oil engine having a 13in centrifugal pump

Further south on the summit pound, Fenny Compton tunnel was another source of delays. In 1838 the opportunity arose to purchase part of the land over the tunnel from Christ Church,

Oxford. The option was taken up following a meeting on 8 August and the college was paid £591. Over the next two years £3,964 was spent in opening up part of the tunnel at both ends and in the middle, leaving two detached sections of 336yd and 452yd.

Traders still continued to complain about the inconvenience to traffic and finally on 13 August 1865 the company decided to open up the southern section. A year later it agreed to do the northern part also. The southern part was ready on 13 June 1868, and the northern part about the beginning of August 1870. The feeder to Wormleighton reservoir had crossed the southern section. When the tunnel was opened the feeder was taken over the cutting in a rectangular open-topped wrought-iron channel on brick piers, which is still there today. The whole of these works had cost £15,000.

At the Oxford end of the canal the company was experiencing considerable competition from coal arriving by other routes, examples being 2,486 tons ex Lydney via the Thames & Severn canal in 1829, and 900 tons from the Somerset coalfields via the Wilts & Berks canal in 1834.[11, 12] In a smaller way it was experiencing the same thing at Eynsham, where even though it refused to allow coal traffic which had passed over the Thames & Severn access to the wharf, coal from the west still reached Eynsham by being unloaded over a meadow adjoining the river. Traders, however, found that no such restrictions applied on the nearby canal to Cassington so, as it was suitable for wide boats, Thames & Severn coal in addition to that from the Oxford began to arrive at this wharf.

The Oxford was powerless to do anything about this situation whilst the tenant paid the rent direct to the Duke of Marlborough, but in the summer of 1834 the company learnt that the tenant, Richard Parker of Witney, was going to quit the wharf at Christmas.[13]

Accordingly on 2 September the Oxford's chairman, Rev D. V. Durell, wrote to the duke's agent asking if it could lease the canal and wharf. A quick exchange of correspondence followed, and a deed was signed in October 1834 whereby the Oxford agreed to a lease for seven years on payment of £45 per annum.[14] The canal at this time was in a sad state of decay; the wharf needed repair, the sill on the lock had gone, the weighbridge was out of order, and the towing path opposite the overflow from the river Evenlode was washed away.

There seems to have been no wharfinger in January 1836 when Messrs Shuffrey and Grove of Witney applied to the Oxford for tenancy. The Oxford had apparently not carried out its part of the agreement, as we find the duke's agent writing a very strong letter of complaint regarding failure to do repairs. Work must eventually have been carried out, as Shuffrey and Grove agreed to take possession from 5 January 1837 and pay £20 per annum. Trade failed to come up to their expectations, and so at the end of the year they moved to Eynsham. The benefits from this move can quickly be seen from the following tonnage receipts paid by them to the Oxford: 1837—£222, 1838—£757.

There appears to have been no further tenant at this wharf till 1841, when John Hambridge took up residence. Finally in October 1842 the Oxford did not renew the lease, so Hambridge took it over on the same terms.[15] He was evidently hard-working and not easily discouraged, for he remained at the wharf for the next seventeen years. At the time of his arrival, the Oxford was still tardy in completing repairs; the duke's agent had to take up this matter with Wood and at length a claim for dilapidations was agreed between the parties.

The Oxford was now at the height of its operations and so it is opportune to give an idea of the services being given on this waterway. Besides coal boats which were the backbone of the trade, numerous other craft moved with full loads of salt, road-stone, iron, etc. A variety of services were offered by carriers for the conveyance of merchandise in small lots. The premier service was by 'fly boats' which operated to a laid down timetable between certain points, calling only at specific wharfs and having priority at locks once they had passed the iron post near the lock with the letters 'DIS'—short for distance. As far as is known no specific service operated on the Oxford purely for passengers. The nearest was the market boat which ran to a timetable and served all points enroute carrying passengers, livestock and goods.

In 1833 consideration was given to a faster means of moving boats and in this connection the Oxford agreed in conjunction with the Grand Junction and Kennet & Avon to purchase from

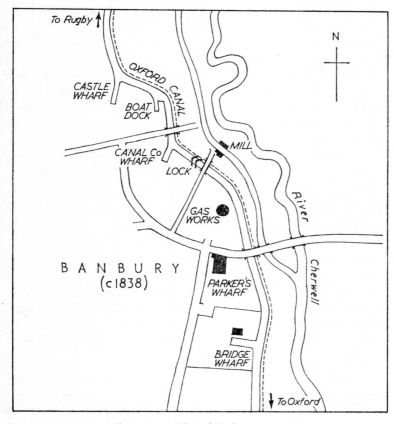

FIGURE 11.   Map of Banbury, 1838

Scotland for £150 a wrought-iron boat known as the *Swallow*. In July this was tried out on part of the Oxford's new line in Barley Fields near Rugby. Afterwards it proceeded on to the Kennet & Avon where it was put into service between Bath & Bathampton.[16]

Banbury was, in the 1830s predominately a market town, where shoemaking and similar trades were prominent. Other occupations such as cheese-making also indicated its importance as a regional centre. The population of some 7,000 people was well served by transport; fly vans operated to London carrying meat and butter and Golby's huge waggons pulled by six or eight horses took the other produce. On the canal two market boats left on Friday mornings carrying goods for Oxford market as well as traffic for onward despatch to Southampton, Portsmouth, the Isle of Wight, Reading and Newbury. In addition another carrier ran to and from Oxford on three days a week, presumably doing the 28-mile journey and loading and unloading in the same day. Samuel Pickford's fly boats called at the Old Wharf on Mondays, Wednesdays, Fridays and Saturdays en route for Oxford carrying traffic from London, Leicester, Manchester, Liverpool, Birmingham, Worcester, Bristol, Sheffield, Derby, Nottingham, Gainsborough, Hull, Boston and Lincoln. On the return journey they took traffic to Braunston where it was transhipped into craft which had come from London.

Another firm, Crowley, Hicklin & Co operated a service on Tuesdays, Thursdays and Saturdays to London, Liverpool, Manchester, Chester, Bristol, Derby, Worcester, Gainsborough, Birmingham, Wolverhampton, Dudley, Warwick, the Potteries, North and South Wales. Lastly Parker & Co ran a fly boat to London via the Thames route which left on Mondays, Wednesdays, Thursdays and Saturdays.[17]

The following facts give a very clear indication of the sheer volume of craft which were using the canal. In 1842, 20,859 boats passed through Hillmorton locks, 9,900 passed over Claydon summit and 14,515 passed to and from the Warwick & Napton

Plate 21 Heyfield Hut wharf in about 1890. This was the first wharf on the canal to be opened within the city of Oxford

Plate 22 Floating chapel moored near Hythe bridge, Oxford, on the Thames beside the canal's towing path in about 1850

Plate 23 Narrow boat *Fanny* owned by William Ward of Oxford moored opposite Worcester College grounds in about 1850 at Oxford

Plate 24 The canal and Thames at Hythe bridge, Oxford, 1835

using in their transit 11,149 locks of water.[18] In this connection the workmen on the canal used to sing this ditty when hedge-laying etc,

> There's a boat comin' up
> There's a boat coming down
> There's one in the lock
> and another in the Pound.

Coal, as mentioned earlier, was the principal commodity being moved on the canal and in 1843 the following tonnages passed by the Hawkesbury Junction toll office southbound.

Coalfield	Tonnage
Cannock/Staffs	22,370
Warwickshire	58,280
Leicestershire	61,250[19]

Legislation regarding numbers and conditions for the people who worked on canal boats was almost non existent at this time and their spiritual and general well-being was forgotten save by the Church. Such was the position in Oxford till 1839 when Henry Ward, a prosperous coal merchant who traded on the Oxford, decided to hand over one of his boats for conversion as a floating chapel for boatmen on the river Thames and canal. In September he approached the Oxford for a subscription and it agreed to pay £20 per annum, being the largest subscriber.

The project came to fruition on 29 December 1839, when the floating chapel was licensed by Bishop Bagot of Oxford. Five trustees were appointed: Archdeacon of Oxford, Vicar of St Mary Magdalen, Curate of St Thomas, W. Ward coal merchant, Richard Cox coal merchant.

The treasurer, W. Ward, was responsible for looking after the donations and subscriptions, not to mention the £100 with which H. Ward endowed the chapel, and these provided the income to pay for the minister, school master and mistress. The chaplain was E. Miller, a Fellow of New College, and the chapel warden William Round, another coal merchant.[20]

On Hogger's map of 1850 the chapel-boat is clearly shown as

G

being moored on the Thames weir stream, which flows down to the castle, by the overflow weir from the canal on the towing path just west of Hythe bridge, Oxford. Services were held on Sunday afternoons and Wednesday evenings. There was also school during the week, and by 1849 Sunday school was being attended by about 100 children. In the wooden turret was a bell used to summon boat people.

During 1868-9 a new chapel called 'St Nicholas' was built at 42 Hythe Bridge Street, to replace the boat which over the years had gradually decayed until one night it quietly sank, having, as H. W. Taunt the well-known Oxford bookseller and publisher said 'fulfilled its mission'.[21] The Oxford continued for a while to support the new chapel though in 1874 it reduced its subscription to £10 and finally in 1902 when asked to raise this sum it decided to cease payments altogether.

The coming of the railways with their steam traction became a serious contender for traffic, but traders on the canals also started to use small steam engines mounted near the rear of a narrow boat to replace the ubiquitous horse. As early as 1826 a steam boat passed over part of the Oxford en route from London to Birmingham to be followed two years later by one from London to Manchester.

Banbury, however, has a special place in history regarding steam driven pleasure boats. For it was here in 1841 that a high pressure non-condensing engine constructed by Henry Warringer about 1840, was fitted to a launch called *Firefly* made in 1839. This engine, which is preserved in the Science Museum in London, has a pair of horizontal oscillating cylinders, 3in diameter by 6in stroke, and the slide valve is worked by single eccentrics in combination with systems of levers and links. *Firefly* was 22ft long, and 4.75ft wide with a draught of 1.67ft. It did not stay long on the Oxford, but was transferred to a tributary of the Cherwell, called the Sor Brook near Bodicote where it was continued to be used until well after the middle of the last century.[22]

CHAPTER 6

Railway competition

WHERE circumstances were against canal building, tramways—
the forerunner of railways—were often built to connect collieries to a wharf or quay. The natural course of events soon took
place; tramways improved and soon came to be built where
canals might earlier have been constructed.

The use to which tramways could be put was shown in 1820
when William James (1771–1837), the owner of collieries at
West Bromwich, Swadlincote in Leicestershire and Wyken—
served by a branch from the Oxford—issued a prospectus. This
showed a line from London to Stratford-upon-Avon via Oxford
with a branch to Wyken.[1]

This was quickly followed in 1821 by the Stratford-upon-
Avon Company which contributed to a survey for a tramway
from its canal at Stratford to the Thames at Eynsham. Only that
part from Stratford to Moreton-in-Marsh materialised and was
opened on 5 September 1826. The Oxford now got its first taste
of railway competition and in consequence had to institute
drawbacks on coal carted to Chipping Norton from Banbury.[2]

The real danger to canals was not really spelt out till the
Bridgewater felt the effect of the opening of the Liverpool &
Manchester railway in 1830. By this time the Oxford had already
taken steps to improve its northern section, but quite obviously
this was not going to stop people promoting railways through
the area which the canal served once they read about the improvement in travel as compared with the coach. The quicker
transit for merchandise was not lost upon them either.

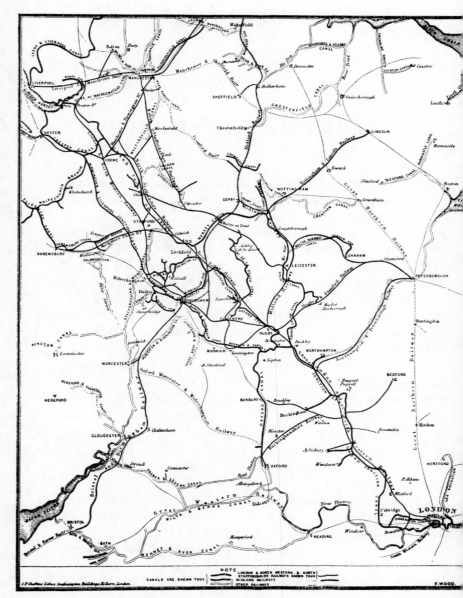

FIGURE 12. Map of canals and railways, 1853

Even before the alterations had been contemplated, initial thoughts were being given to a railway between Birmingham and London. In 1826 Sir John Rennie published a plan for a route to London via Southam, Banbury and Oxford.[3] However, money was short so nothing resulted. A year later another plan was prepared, this time by Francis Giles which showed a route via Coventry and Rugby. The rival groups joined forces on 11 September 1830 after George and Robert Stephenson had surveyed the two routes. They reported in favour of the one via Coventry and Rugby, which differed only in detail from that originally put forward by Francis Giles. The promoters quickly followed up the report and on 12 January 1831 plans were deposited for the proposed London & Birmingham railway. It met with a storm of vigorous opposition, not only from the Grand Junction, with whose line the railway was to run virtually parallel for many miles, but from a large number of landowners and from those who had their livelihood from the traffic on the roads. The busy Watling Street was directly threatened and the road coach proprietors, waggoners and their supporting industries such as posting inns and stables all joined in the outcry. Despite the efforts of the Grand Junction and the Oxford the Bill passed the House of Commons in June 1832, but the opposition of numerous landowners resulted in its failure in the House of Lords. The Oxford was by now very much aware of the damage that the building of this railway would do to the receipts on its northern section. Accordingly when the committee met on 8 February they agreed to raise money to oppose the next Bill. This was introduced later in the year and quickly passed through all its stages and received the Royal Assent. The opposing landowners were placated by offers giving them treble the value of their land taken for the railway. The first effect as far as the Oxford was concerned came in July 1837 when carriers from Banbury started taking London traffic by road to Wolverton for placing on rail. Then on 9 April 1838 the line was opened from Birmingham to Rugby and from 24 June right through to

London, but this was only for passengers. Goods traffic was not carried till 12 November 1838.

That the worst fears of the Oxford were well founded can easily be judged from the toll receipts at Braunston, the interchange point with the Grand Junction on the route to London: 1838—£33,277; 1839—£29,922; 1840—£23,859; 1841—£19,852.

Rugby's claim to fame at this time was its privilege of holding no less than eleven fairs during the year and a large cattle market on Saturdays. The town of over 4,000 people, which included the famous public school, was served by only two coal merchants on the end of the branch at Rugby wharf, most of the business being done at Hillmorton on the main line. Before the coming of the railway in 1833 £311 was taken at this toll office. However during the period of railway construction takings gradually rose to £526 in 1836, but by 1840 following the opening of the railway takings had fallen to £316.

The Great Western Railway's prospectus of 1833 showed a branch line from Didcot to Oxford, which if built would effect the Oxford's trade since quite a lot of traffic from London came up the Grand Junction and down the Oxford from Napton rather than use the Thames which still had navigational difficulties. In fact the Lord Mayor of London had experienced these difficulties several years earlier in 1826 when he made an official journey from Oxford to London. The report on his progress between Abingdon and Wallingford states:

> The navigation here appeared to be particularly defective for, with all the advantages of the exertions that had been made by the Water-Bailiff's directions, and the expense that had been incurred for the supply of water; the country having been comparatively drained for several miles along the upper districts,—and though the City Barge and Shallop, and the attendant boats, drew scarcely more than two feet of water,—they were detained at Clifton a considerable length of time.[4]

The canal company was, however, well supported in Oxford and with the assistance of the city council and the university it succeeded in defeating successive Bills for the branch in the years 1835–7–8 and 1840. Even so by 1840 carriers from Oxford were taking their traffic to Steventon station situated 10 miles away on the main line from London to Bristol.⁵

Finally in 1843 the Great Western Railway Act for the branch to Oxford was passed despite opposition led by the warden of Wadham college. Work was quickly put in hand and the branch was opened on 12 June 1844. Since the tonnage receipts taken by the canal at Oxford only involved a small amount of traffic to and from London it is not surprising to find that due to a general increase in business the receipts actually increased after the opening of the branch. 1843—£17,556; 1844—£18,482; 1845—£20,134; 1846—£20,865; 1847—£21,132. The main loss of revenue was in fact felt by the Thames Commissioners.

To provide a connection for traffic to and from Banbury John Weaving extended his market boat working out on to the Thames to Friars wharf below Osney lock which was adjacent to the original GWR station.

Another railway which was soon destined to effect the Oxford's receipts was the Midland Counties. This project was first mooted at a meeting on 16 August 1832 held in The Sun at Eastwood, Nottinghamshire and its Act was passed for a line from Derby and Nottingham to Leicester and Rugby. Even before the line was opened on 1 July 1840, the Midland Counties had asked the London & Birmingham if it would accept coal at Rugby for London to which its superintendent is reputed to have said, 'What, coal by railway, they's be asking us to carry dung next.' Already the Midland Counties had paid the Oxford £800 for moving Rugby wharf and for an exchange of land as its line passed the end of the wharf branch.⁶ Transhipping facilities between rail and canal were therefore made and on 9 March 1842 the Oxford brought in a special rate for coal between there and the Grand Junction of 7½p per ton. The Midland Counties began to develop this trade in earnest by introducing a special rate of ½p per ton per mile in July 1843 to anyone sending more than 8,000 tons a year between Derby and Rugby. Not surprisingly on 20 December the Midland Counties was asking that the wharf facilities be enlarged to allow four boats to be loaded at the same time. By 1845 special arrangements existed for this traffic to be gauged at Hillmorton, Braunston and Paddington. Coal, however, was not the only traffic the Midland Counties put on water at Rugby; merchandise such as silk from Macclesfield was loaded on to Pickford's boats to make the last part of the journey to Coventry.

The receipts at Hillmorton rose from the 1840 level of £316 to £462 in 1842, but once the Midland Counties had made its peace with the London & Birmingham takings fell away sharply to £160 in 1850.

Although the Oxford was feeling the effects of the railways, its £100 shares still fetched more than its railway rivals in 1842. Comparative stock exchange prices were as follows: Oxford canal—£600; London & Birmingham Railway—£180; Great Western Railway—£89.

Other railways which would eventually effect the Oxford were promoted in 1844. In Banbury J. A. Gillett, a banker in Banbury and Oxford, presided at a meeting of over 600 people at which four rival plans for railways to the town were discussed.[7] The meeting approved the Oxford–Rugby project, a Great Western Railway subsidiary company, which obtained its Act in the following year. Construction was very slow and it was not till 2 September 1850 that the line was opened from Oxford to Banbury with intermediate stations at Aynho, Heyford, and Woodstock Road (Bletchingdon). The canal was crossed in many places and as a result the Oxford received £32,326.90 to cover compensation, purchase of land and the public house at Aynho. Although this line ran parallel to the canal it had little effect on its receipts until it was extended northwards through Warwick to Birmingham for freight traffic from February 1853.

Towards the end of 1852 very serious flooding took place around Oxford and the temporary cessation of canal traffic and the effect of the recent railway opening to Banbury resulted in John Weaving's market boat between Oxford and Banbury finishing altogether, this despite the fact that the other inter-mediate stations at Kidlington and Somerton were not opened till 1855 whilst King's Sutton was as late as 1872.

Another line, however, which entered Banbury from the east was to have a far more serious impact. This was the Bucking-hamshire railway authorised in 1846 and opened to Banbury on 1 May 1850. Repercussions were soon felt; the Oxford heard on 19 June that the canal traders were not laying in the usual level of stocks, so it ordered its wharfinger to purchase coal and sell it later at a price to be advised by the company. The coal traders complained of this action so the Oxford reduced its rates for coal to Banbury by 80 per cent.[8]

As this railway was constructed southwards its effect was felt elsewhere. The opening of Bicester station reduced the tonnage dealt with over the wharf at Heyford, whence waggons drawn by up to six horses took coal to Piddington, Brill and Ludgershall villages as well as Bicester. The scene at the wharf must have presented quite a busy picture with up to twenty teams awaiting loading. The overseers of the workhouse at Bicester kept their costs down to an absolute minimum as it was the practice for the inmates to take wheelbarrows for the 7 miles to Heyford wharf to collect their coal.[9]

At Eynsham the Oxford had taken action to strengthen its position. On 24 June 1845 it purchased the Talbot Inn from R. C. Toner, a butcher and overseer, for £420; and on 20 Feb-ruary 1849 the wharf and Clay weir from J. R. Jammett, a grocer, for £850, it having been leased previously from him for £60 per annum. The first railborne coal to compete with the wharf trade was that from the Buckinghamshire railway station at Stratfield Brake (which was opened in 1850) on the Oxford–Banbury road near Kidlington. Worse was to follow in 1853 when the Oxford, Worcester & Wolverhampton railway opened stations at Shipton to serve Burford and at Hanborough to serve

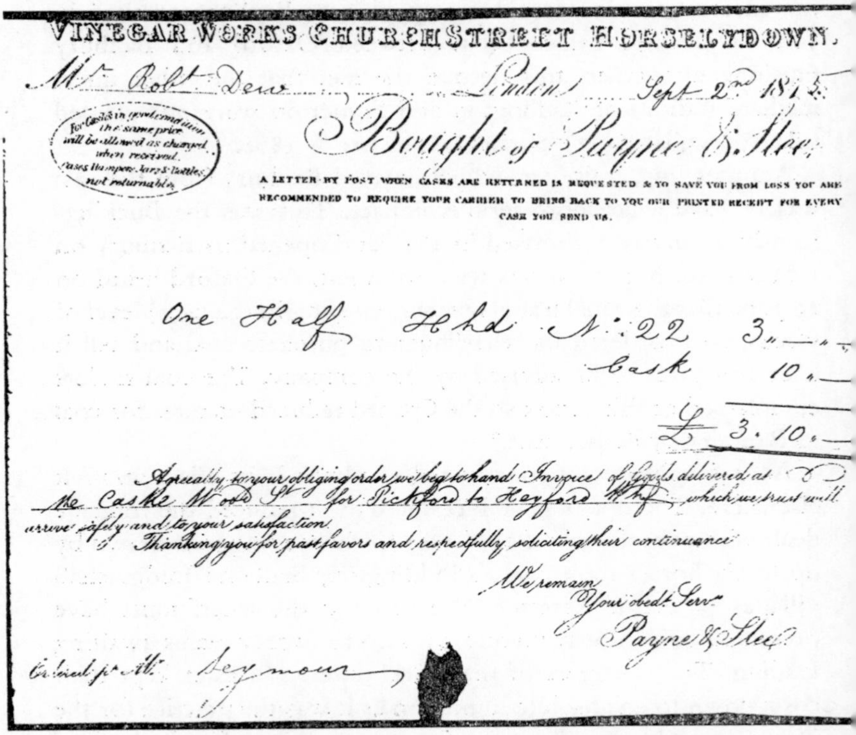

VINEGAR WORKS CHURCH STREET HORSELYDOWN.

Mr. Robt. Dew London Sept 2nd 1845

Bought of Payne & Slee.

For Casks in good condition the same price will be allowed as charged when received. Cases Hampers Jars & Bottles not returnable.

A LETTER BY POST WHEN CASKS ARE RETURNED IS REQUESTED & TO SAVE YOU FROM LOSS YOU ARE RECOMMENDED TO REQUIRE YOUR CARRIER TO BRING BACK TO YOU OUR PRINTED RECEIPT FOR EVERY CASK YOU SEND US.

One Half Hhd No. 22	3 " — " —
Cask	10 " —
	£ 3. 10. —

Agreeably to your obliging order we beg to hand Invoice of Goods delivered at the Caske Wood St for Pickford to Heyford Whf, which we trust will arrive safely and to your satisfaction.

Thanking you for past favors and respectfully soliciting their continuance

We remain
Your obedt. Servts.
Payne & Slee

Ordered pr. Mr. Seymour

FIGURE 13. Bill for vinegar to Heyford, 1845

Witney. These caused the tonnage receipts on Eynsham traffic to fall by 64 per cent between 1849 and 1854. In consequence the Oxford looked to see if staff or wages could be reduced; it decided otherwise, so the wharfinger, Philip Scholey junior, continued to receive 50p weekly and his assistant, J. Waller, 25p. Scholey's father was the Talbot innkeeper.

Down at Oxford the Buckinghamshire railway had asked its parent company—the London & North Western—for help over the siting and access to the proposed terminal. Once the site was agreed, how to cross the Sheepwash channel which connected the

Thames with the Oxford at Isis lock had to be settled. The Thames Commissioners were consulted and at the Buckingham-shire's committee meeting on 11 July 1850 the well-known personality from Euston, none other than Captain Huish, attended and stated his views.[10] They settled for a swing bridge which, when built, measured 50ft × 22ft with a width at water level of 13ft 2in. They also built a towing path bridge over the Thames backwater by the side of Isis lock which saved having to take the horses into Oxford, along the Botley road and up the Thames from Osney bridge. In July 1851 the Buckinghamshire railway built a siding to a wharf on the Thames backwater for £200, presumably to facilitate the conveyance of its traffic by water to points served by the Great Western railway.[11]

A frequent event, when a canal's future was being threatened by railway promotion in its area, was for the canal to be purchased by the railway. This happened in the case of the Ashby. In 1846 the Midland railway purchased the canal, the acquisition being confirmed by an Act.[12] To obtain this Act the Midland had to agree to a number of clauses being inserted to protect the Coventry and Oxford's interests. The latter was particularly concerned since over 79,000 tons of coal passed from the Ashby to the Oxford in 1845, some of this passing over the entire length of the canal. In this Act were two clauses to protect canal interests which were of special benefit to the Oxford. One specifically stated that 'if owing to railway competition, coal from Moira collieries is diverted from the Oxford canal, and in order to meet such diversion the Oxford canal lowers its tolls to 5p for this traffic, then the Midland railway must lower its tolls on the Ashby canal proportionally, provided that the tolls shall not be reduced below $\frac{1}{16}$p per ton per mile'. The other stated that if one or more canals on the route to London combined to reduce their rates then the Midland railway must reduce its tolls on the Ashby correspondingly. These clauses ensured fair and reasonable competition and in consequence an appreciable tonnage of coal continued to pass on to the Oxford. The Oxford by this means was able to achieve a continued high level of traffic though it had to keep a careful eye on the Midland. In 1874 for instance, acting on information received from the Moira collieries it complained that the level of water in the Ashby was below normal as a result of it being taken from the canal for the use of locomotives on both the Midland and London & North Western railways. The Midland installed a pump into a well with a meter so that the level corresponded with that of the Coventry at Marston Junction.

During 1852 only 10,900 tons passed through Isis lock on to the Thames, but by 1863–4 a considerable improvement had been effected.

Destination	1863	1864
Abingdon	7,140 tons	6,887 tons
Sutton Courtenay	957 ,,	891 ,,
Dorchester	556 ,,	699 ,,
Shillingford	658 ,,	1,039 ,,
Benson	153 ,,	191 ,,
Crowmarsh	249 ,,	651 ,,
Warborough	688 ,,	680 ,,
Wallingford	3,610 ,,	3,758 ,,
Pangbourne	2,078 ,,	1,190 ,,
Wantage	NIL	313 ,,
TOTALS	16,089	16,298 [13]

The northern end of the Oxford, together with part of the Coventry and the whole of the Ashby, comprises over 37 miles of canal on one level with only 'stop locks' to impede the free passage of boats. Indeed on the 54 miles between Moira colliery at the most northern end of the Ashby and Braunston, where the Oxford joins the Grand Junction, there are only the three locks at Hillmorton. Generally speaking canal routes do not lend themselves to strings of barges being towed by a tug, but the circumstances in this area resulted in serious experiments being carried out, litigation against their operation and eventual success.

In 1856 a 6hp steam boat, called *Pioneer*, moved by a double-screw 'Sourabaya' propeller, which had been invented by John Inshaw of Birmingham, was purchased for the conveyance of coals from the Moira Colliery to London. This boat could travel at the same rate as that attained by horse traction and without making any more swell than a boat towed in the ordinary way; and it was capable of being used as a tug, and drawing after it a fleet of several boats.

The directors of the Grand Junction, Coventry and Oxford canals, which *Pioneer* had to traverse on its way to London, found that it really did not injure the canal banks, and were, of course, glad to have this new agency at work on their waters. But there was another canal, along which it was necessary to pass in the journey from Moira—the Ashby; and this was in the hands of the Midland railway. It was not to be expected that a railway would look with much favour on the scheme, designed entirely to promote canal interests. That the *Pioneer* was refused admission within the bounds over which it had control was therefore not surprising. If it had been able to make good its refusal, anything like a general introduction of steam on canals would have been impractical, because, whenever one of the waterways happened to be in the possession of a railway, the chain would be broken. But it so happened that when Parliament granted powers and privileges to canal companies, it also imposed upon them liabilities and responsibilities, and these devolve upon anybody who purchases the privileges. It was contended that the railway was not at liberty to refuse the admission of a steam boat, which would do no more harm than one drawn by a horse; and that the whole question should be fairly tested before a legal tribunal. Messrs Woodcock and Twist, of Coventry, were selected to conduct the suit. Charles Woodcock of the firm, being clerk to the Coventry, was one of the ablest and staunchest defenders of the interests of canals in their severest struggles.

A Bill was filed in Chancery for an injunction to restrain the Midland railway from preventing the navigation of the Ashby

by the *Pioneer* steam boat. The railway did not display any remarkable vigour in endeavouring to obtain a speedy decision;
but the suit was carried on with the greatest energy on the part
of the plaintiffs, and not a single delay was allowed where it
could be avoided. The matter was argued before the Master of
the Rolls in the early part of 1859. An eminent engineer, W. Pole,
was appointed to make experiments, and report whether *Pioneer*
could navigate the Ashby without doing any more injury than
would be caused by a boat drawn by a horse—that being the only
question he had to consider.[14]

He accordingly tried the experiments in the month of May
1859, with the *Pioneer*. This was of the ordinary size used on the
canal, namely, about 70ft long, 7ft wide, and 4ft deep. It had been
fitted by Mr Inshaw with a small steam engine of 6hp, working
twin screws at the stern; the machinery took up little room, and
left a large portion of the boat available for cargo: the boat was
also intended to be used, if necessary, for towing. The experiments comprised many different varieties of conditions, in regard
to the loading of the steamboat herself, and the number of other
boats she had in tow; and the speed attained varied from $1\frac{1}{4}$ to 5
miles per hour, this speed varying, not only with the work done,
but also with the section of the canal, as it was found that where
the canal was diminished in sectional area the speed was retarded,
and vice versa.

The principal object of investigation was to observe the wave,
or surge, caused by the passage of the steamer, and to estimate
the effect it would have on the banks of the canal. It was well
known that any vessel propelled through a confined channel
would produce, in passing, a wave or oscillation of the surface of
the water, which would probably, in some shape or other, reach
the banks, and cause an agitation of the water in contact with
them. The magnitude and character of this agitation would,
however, depend on the velocity and the other circumstances of
the case. It might be so trifling as to be practically harmless, or it
might take such a form as to be capable, if frequently repeated, of

producing much injury. These two conditions merged so gradually into each other, that it was difficult to define the exact limit where the harmless state ended and the injurious one began; but, after careful observation, Mr Pole was led to define the commencement of the injurious action to take place when the wave began to assume a breaking form, as distinguished from a convex shape, or wave of translation; and he conceived that when a continuous wave possessing this character in a marked degree accompanied the boat, injury to the banks, if not protected by masonry, or otherwise, must in time be expected to occur.

This point being fixed, observations were directed to the character of the wave produced at different speeds; but it then became necessary to draw a distinction between two causes, by either or both of which waves might be produced. These were, first, the actual passage of the boat through the water, which would be independent of the means of propulsion; and secondly, the action on the water of the propelling apparatus itself, which was capable, under certain circumstances, of creating a wave more formidable than that due simply to the motion of the body. Now it was a very decided result of these experiments, that the method of propulsion, by the double screw, did not, of itself, at any speed attained, give rise to any wave or surge at all injurious to the banks of the canal. The two screws caused, of course, an agitation of the water in their wake, but this did not extend to the banks in any such form as could damage them. This second cause of wave was therefore dismissed from consideration. There then remained the wave arising from the passage of the boat through the water. This varied in some degree with the section of the canal, and with the occurrence of curves in its direction; but it principally depended on the speed, and the following were the general results obtained. Up to a speed of 3 miles an hour no wave of an injurious character appeared. Between 3 miles and 3½ miles an hour a breaking wave appeared occasionally in curves and shallows. Above 3½ miles an hour the breaking wave became more continuous, and took a more marked character. At 4 miles an hour the injurious character of the wave became very decided. At 5 miles an hour, even in a much enlarged section, the wave was still more increased, breaking sometimes over the towing path, and being followed by other waves in succession.[15]

Mr Pole did not find, in the course of these experiments, that the use of the steamer, with ordinary care, caused any injurious interference with general navigation by other boats. It had the advantage of the absence of a tow line, and of being able to pass on either side other boats at pleasure. The only inconvenience he could imagine was in case a tug was made to draw a long train of boats at a very slow speed, by which the passage of other traffic through narrow bridges, or tunnels, or locks, might be delayed. The result of the investigation was to lead Mr Pole to recommend that steamboats should be admitted upon the canal subject to such a limitation of their speed as would avoid the production of an injurious wave; and this recommendation was made an order of the Court of Chancery. The payment of a heavy bill of costs, incurred by the plaintiffs, was one of the disagreeable incidents which happened to the Midland as a result of this suit.

In August 1860, a steam tug intended for traffic between Moira and Coventry was launched. This one, of 14hp, named *Volunteer*, had been built for the Coventry and Moira colliery. Like the *Pioneer*, there were two screws placed on each side of the boat, near the stern, which was hollowed out for them about 3ft 6in below the surface of the water.

On 15 August 1860 *Pioneer* was tested between Moira and Rugby, and from thence to Braunston. It was found capable of drawing four loaded narrow boats at a rate of about 3 miles per hour, and 5 miles per hour when empty. *Pioneer* passed Rugby wharf about 15.00, and having reached Braunston returned to Rugby wharf about 21.00, and started at 05.00 the next day on its homeward voyage under the command of John Bird.[16]

These experiments were so successful that as from 2 October 1863 steamboats started operating to a laid-down schedule towing between four and ten boats each with a steerer.

Plate 25 Details of the headstone of the Oxford canal company's offices at Oxford

Plate 26 Canal company's office, Oxford, 1943

Plate 27 New road coal wharf, Oxford, 1927

Plate 28 SY *Firefly*, which was launched onto the canal at Banbury in 1839, shown on the Soar brook which feeds the river Cherwell

Mon, Wed, Fri			Tu, Thur, Sat		
Braunston	dep	10.30	Hawkesbury		
Hillmorton	dep	12.30	Junction	dep	07.00
Rugby Arm	dep	13.30	Stretton Wharf	dep	09.30
Stretton Wharf	dep	15.30	Rugby Arm	dep	12.00
Hawkesbury			Hillmorton	dep	13.45
Junction	arr	17.30	Braunston	arr	16.15[17]

The tug *Pioneer* was not withdrawn from service till 1870.

In 1864 no less than 4,600 boats left Moira and Church Gresley wharves on the Ashby. It was considered that towing by tug reduced the costs by 50 per cent. Rates per boat from Hawkesbury were 18¾p to Stretton wharf, 30p to Rugby, 37½p to Hillmorton and 52½p to Braunston.

The coal trade became increasingly difficult, but the Oxford still refused to allow coal off other canals to come on to it; in 1846 for example the Wilts & Berks asked for coal rates to Heyford but the Oxford played it cleverly by not replying.

From its junction with the Coventry for the first few miles the canal passed through part of the Warwickshire coalfield. Several shafts were sunk close to the canal and it was necessary to keep a careful watch for subsidence. Others such as the Victoria colliery, situated near where Coventry's power station is today located, had a small tramway leading to a wharf on the Oxford between Longford and Hawkesbury Junction. Another was Craven colliery which had an edge-rail tramway, along what is now known as Woodway Lane, to a wharf on the canal by the first stone bridge (No 7). Both collieries were affected by the London & North Western railway's proposal (published on 12 November 1847) for a 2½ mile branch to Craven colliery. Strangely enough when the Oxford's clerk, Mr E. W. Lee, was asked for his comments, he made no objection. The Bill was introduced into the House of Commons on 3 February 1848, quickly passed through all its stages and received the Royal Assent on 14 August in the same year. Work was soon started and the line was opened during 1848.

H

By 1852 the position was so bad that the Oxford tried to reach agreement with the London & North Western on coal rates to Banbury and Oxford in the hope that the rate could be held at 17p. The railway would not sign the agreement and the upshot was that the Oxford had to reduce its rate from Hawkesbury to 13p per ton. The railway reached Abingdon on 2 June 1856 and from 9 May 1861 coal started to reach Eynsham on the partially completed Witney railway.

The state of the Thames in the early 1860s was at its worst ever. Due to lack of dredging, boats coming off the Oxford through Duke's cut often had to pay the Eynsham weir keeper 10¾p for a 'flash' of water. The gates at King's weir were kept in good order as this was the responsibility of Wolvercote paper mill, but the pound below was so shallow that for at least ten years boats had moved between Eynsham and points on the river below Oxford by using the canal between Duke's and Isis locks for which the Oxford charged 25p per boat. Normally boats could only get away down river from Oxford on Mondays and Thursdays when a 'flash' was given.[18] It was not unknown for millers on the Thames who controlled a weir by a lock to hold back water till they required it with consequent grounding of boats on the shallows thereby created down river. To overcome this problem the weir owners were required by law at certain stipulated times to open the sluices for two three-hourly periods each week to give a 'flash' of water for navigational purposes. Quite often during the period of the 'flash' the mill had to cease work.

The Thames Commissioners were in very bad financial straits. So much so that in 1865 the Oxford deposited £150 in the Old Bank in an account called 'Thames Navigation Repair Fund' which was only to be used in the event of any emergency works being required on the Thames between Oxford and Wallingford. In the same year the company generously allowed materials for repair of works on the Thames to pass free of tolls.

The state of the Thames became the subject of a Royal Commission in 1866 and this resulted in the Thames Navigation Act of the same year. The Thames Conservancy quickly took action; Osney lock was rebuilt, the timber towing path bridge over the Sheepwash channel with two piers was renewed with a single span of iron making it easier for boats passing to and from the Oxford, the channel was dredged and the towing path repaired. Trade responded quickly. Toll receipts at Osney lock in respect of traffic to and from the Oxford rose from £849.37 in 1867 to £871.57 in 1868 and in 1869 reached £924.86. This was helped by the fact that in times of flood the Thames Conservancy's tug at Abingdon towed empty boats back to the canal.

The Oxford University Press, the lessees of Wolvercote paper mill, bought two narrow boats in 1856, which plied by turns between Wolvercote and collieries in the Midlands until, refusing to meet demands for higher wages from the boatmen, the delegates sold them in 1916. In 1884 coal was thus brought from Moira colliery in Leicestershire to the wharf behind the mill at a cost of 66½p a ton, the price delivered by rail and cart being 1½p more. By 1897 the price had risen to 72p when about 100 tons of coal were being used each week.[19]

Although the fortunes of the canal had changed over the years as will be seen from the table given below, nevertheless, there was still a considerable level of business and despite railway competition the company had in 1848 paid off the remaining part of the loans, some of which dated from the early part of the century.

Year	Gross Tonnage	Revenue (£)	Dividends Amount (£)	%	Loan Interest Paid (£)
1828	450,000	89,300	60,740	34	2,020
1838	520,000	86,600	53,594	30	4,914
1848	420,000	56,000	35,729	20	277
1858	400,000	24,700	14,291	8¼	—
1868	482,000	24,700	15,185	8¾	— [20]

The staff actually employed on the canal as at 1 September 1853 shows that numbers were being kept down to a bare minimum.

Section	Labourers	Masons	Carpenters	Blacksmiths	Lock-keepers	TOTALS
Longford–Stretton	4	–	–	–	–	4
Stretton–Newbold	7	1	1	–	–	9
Newbold–Hillmorton	4	–	–	–	–	4
Hillmorton–Barby	6	–	3	1	4	14
Barby–Shuckburgh	3	–	–	–	–	3
Shuckburgh–Napton	2	–	–	–	2	4
Napton–Wormleighton	5	1	1	–	2	9
Wormleighton–Banbury	8	1	1	1	4	15
Banbury–Heyford	5	1	1	–	4	11
Heyford–Oxford	7	3	1	–	5	16
TOTALS	51	7	8	2	21	89

In fact nearly two-thirds of the staff were employed on the southern section which had the smallest amount of traffic.

From time immemorial traffic had moved on all days of the week, but following the national trend to reduce working hours in the Victorian age, it was decided in March 1875, despite the need to offset railway competition, to close the section from Napton to Oxford between 19.00 Saturday and 04.00 Monday in summer and between 21.00 Saturday and 05.00 Monday in winter.

In 1877 the Canal Boats Act was passed which required all boats with living accommodation to register with a local authority who would issue a certificate stating the number of adults and children who could live on the boat. The registers compiled in 1879 by towns on or near the Oxford give an indication of the number of boats which possibly traded on the canal:

Abingdon—15; Coventry—116; Oxford—49; Banbury—74; Hinckley—36; Warwick—78.

The Board of Trade in 1894 secured an Act which dealt with canal rates and one of the items deleted the clauses in the Oxford's original Act concerning the collection of tolls by the Coventry for the first two miles on the Oxford and likewise by the Oxford for the first two miles on the Coventry.

As late as 1905 some long hauls were still being undertaken by carriers which involved journeys over the Oxford, down the Thames and on to the Kennet & Avon.

Coal	Coventry to Burghfield Mill, Reading
Coal	Coventry to Huntley & Palmers, Reading
Coal	Coventry to Colthrop mill, Thatcham
Coal	Coventry to Aldermaston
Coal	Coventry to Newbury
Corn	Stratford-on-Avon to Colthrop mill, Thatcham
Plaster	Barrow-on-Soar to Colthrop mill, Thatcham
Hides	Birmingham to Reading tannery[21]

In all 12,671 tons passed through Isis lock on to the Thames and in the reverse direction 6,939 tons consisting mainly of coke, tar, hay and ballast.[22] Even to maintain this level of business it had been necessary for the Oxford to make toll reductions—coal off the Coventry to the Thames 8p per ton instead of 11p, and materials off the Warwick & Napton to the Thames 6p instead of 9p. Above Oxford movement was at a very low ebb. Only twice a week did a boat reach the Rose Revived wharf at Newbridge with coal from Moira colliery. Coal and roadstone from Nuneaton still came to Eynsham and in the summer the boats returned with hay and straw from Thames-side farms for sale in the Midlands.

In all this atmosphere of railway competition there was one bright spot. At the turn of the century a short privately owned canal about 600yd long was made to the Alexandra colliery off the branch canal to Wyken Old colliery in Warwickshire, which had only been used between 1820 and 1850. Even so it was worked out by 1912.

Traffic to and from the Grand Junction was keeping up remarkably well; in 1908 6,790 pairs of boats passed through Braunston locks and a further 1,555 single boats, in all carrying about 295,000 tons. There was quite a lot of empty running too; 2,790 boats passed empty going northwards and a further 512 southwards.[23]

Like other canals the Oxford was finding that it was still possible to increase local traffic, but not enough to offset the loss on
other traffic. The following tonnage table for the Oxford bears
out this statement.

	1898	*1905*
Loaded and unloaded on the Oxford	21,003	25,898
Loaded on Oxford and unloaded elsewhere	49,677	29,102
Loaded elsewhere and unloaded on Oxford	94,537	72,794
Through	256,290	250,907
	421,507	378,701[24]

The last years of the nineteenth century saw an ever increasing
interest in waterways due to the general wish to reduce railway
rates especially upon raw materials which were of prime interest
to British industry. The Associated Chambers of Commerce
introduced several Bills into Parliament between 1901 and 1906
which culminated in the government of the day setting up a
Royal Commission. This eventually reported in 1910.

Many facets were examined and various suggestions made such
as the one by A. J. Harberton, a member of the committee of
enquiry, who wanted the Oxford improved between Oxford and
Fenny Compton and a new canal made from there across to the
Warwick & Napton near Leamington Spa. The Grand Junction
which had been pressing for the widening of the northern part of
the Oxford since 1794 now took the opportunity to mention that
it would cost £653,332 to widen the Oxford for the 26½ miles
between Napton and Hawkesbury.

The report recommended that the canal between London and
Birmingham should be modernised to take barges capable of
carrying 100 tons; a narrow boat normally conveyed only between
25 and 30 tons. The scheme was costed in detail by Sir John
Wolfe Barry and Partners who estimated that £67,827 would be
required to straighten the canal between Calcutt locks on the
Warwick & Napton and Lower Shuckburgh on the Oxford and

provide a new two-way junction at Napton to avoid the sharp curve. Alternatively if the canal was to pass barges capable of carrying 300 tons then the estimate would be £144,761.

Listed among the details in the voluminous report on the Oxford between Napton and Braunston were no less than seventeen bridges with a minimum of 8ft headroom, five culverts all at least 7ft below water level and five wharves all in private ownership. Of the four overflow weirs three were of 16ft in length, the other at Braunston was exceptional being 30ft long with removable flash boards and a flash paddle. At Braunston the stop-lock was 8ft 2in wide and 100ft long, both measurements being well in excess of narrow boat requirements. All in all this 5 mile length of canal would seem to have been in excellent condition, though no mention was made of the state of the banks or towing path and it would seem therefore no special attention had been given to this feature. The surprisingly good depth of water under the bridges of 4ft 6in can be attributed to the Grand Junction's dredger which had recently been lent free.

CHAPTER 7

The Search for Life

In the Black Country the railway companies had built many transhipment wharves and from these narrow boats operated to the many works situated alongside the canals. These craft carried out a similar task to that performed today by lorries working to and from railway premises. On the Oxford there was only one instance of this kind of working and that was at Enslow, 11 miles north of Oxford in the Cherwell valley.

During 1906–7 the Oxford Cement Company's works was erected beside the Oxford just north of Pidgeons lock at Kirtlington. There was no access to this site by rail or road; therefore all equipment and building material was sent by water, as was coal, sand and gypsum used for the cement making. A ferry boat was kept to take horses across to the works stables from the towpath. The coal came from Baddesley, Cannock, Exhall, Griff, Measham, Newdigate and Wyken collieries and the seven boatmen employed by the works averaged seven to eight trips per month. Twenty-six tons was the normal payload for a narrow boat and a bonus of 25p per trip was paid on weights over that amount; if underweight a discount of 25p resulted. Coal was unloaded by shovel and barrow and four men would normally handle 52 tons between 07.00 and 16.00 with 30 minutes for lunch.

The tonnage of cement forwarded from the start in 1907 till 1922 was:

Year	Cement Sent Out (Tons)	Year	Cement Sent Out (Tons)
1907	481	1915	13,067
1908	3,680	1916	11,375
1909	3,936	1917	13,577
1910	4,181	1918	11,421
1911	7,984	1919	12,279
1912	8,383	1920	12,835
1913	11,299	1921	11,724
1914	14,072	1922	17,287[1]

Some of this tonnage was taken to Enslow wharf for transfer to the adjacent GWR goods yard at Bletchingdon station in horse-drawn boats named after such local places as Oxford, Banbury and Tackley. The standard livery for these boats was ultramarine framing and white panels with blue lettering and instead of the usual side and top sheets over top planks on stands, they were covered by removable planks resting lengthways on curved frames fastened to its 6in planks built the length of the gunwales, with canvas sheets spread over the whole and held down by jamming the hems with a strip of wood in small brackets above the gunwale. Traffic by rail must have been appreciable as in April 1909 the GWR approached the Oxford with a view to purchasing part of the garden of the wharfinger's house near where the railway line crossed the canal at the end of the goods yard. By November an area of 250 square yards was agreed, for which the GWR paid £40 in April 1910. Finally the GWR included the purchase within its General Powers Act of 1910.

A year later complaint was made that the wharfinger's house was in need of repair. Fifty pounds was spent on it and £100 on new stables for the Rock of Gibraltar, then rented from the Oxford by Halls Brewery of Oxford (now Ind Coope Ltd). The brewery complained about the alterations and applied for the rent to be reduced from £65 to £50 per annum. The matter was finally settled when the Oxford agreed to lease the inn for 21 years at £55 per annum from 1911.

Oxford Canal.

To Lock-Keepers and Boatmen.

TAKE NOTICE, that in consequence of the shortness of water, no Lock shall be drawn off when there is a Boat within sight, or a short distance of it, on its way downwards, but such Boat shall have the use of the Lock before another Boat shall pass upwards.

BY ORDER.

Canal Office, Oxford.

VINCENT, PRINTER, OXFORD.

FIGURE 14.   Notice to lock-keepers and boatmen

During that autumn there was a very severe shortage of water on the summit between Marston Doles and Claydon which resulted in 'waiting turns' having to be operated for fifty-two days between Banbury and Claydon to the north. This meant no boat was allowed to enter a lock unless a boat had previously passed out of it in the opposite direction. The Oxford had hoped that during this sort of drought they would have had a sufficient water supply south of Cropredy, since in 1905 they had purchased Cropredy mill on the Cherwell which had been out of use since 1892 following a serious fire.[2] The mill stream is on a level with the canal and the pipe connecting them is capable of carrying 250,000 gallons to the canal daily. A few years ago this pipe was blocked and it took eight men pulling on a rope with a chain wrapped around it to extract a quick-thorn bush which was growing inside the pipe. The old pumping engine at Napton had long been out of service and during this period the Oxford hired two steam ploughing traction engines from the Oxford Steam Ploughing Company (now John Allens of Cowley).[3] Above Nell Bridge lock 5 miles south of Banbury the GWR took up to 200,000 gallons of water from the canal for its troughs at Aynho and in dry seasons the Oxford sometimes found it necessary to pump water up from the Cherwell.

Up to 1914, despite railway competition, the Oxford managed to increase the tonnage carried, but the events of World War I resulted in a serious drop from which it never really recovered. As the staff left to join the armed services the Oxford, like other independent canals, could find no replacements so boats stood idle for want of crews, maintenance was cut and unloading took longer. Tonnage and receipts soon fell and by 1917 the situation was so serious that the Government had to assume responsibility for the canals which they did as from 1 March under powers granted within the Defence of the Realm Regulations and Act of 1914. Under it they set up a Canal Control Committee to try and stem the decline and at the same time pay compensation to the canals where their revenue fell short of the 1913 level.

The following Oxford figures speak for themselves:

Year	Tonnage	Compensation (£)
1905	378,698	NA
1913	453,609	NA
1916	364,772	NA
1917	312,454	5,831
1918	321,519	9,742
1919	286,459	14,815[4]

The canal system was controlled by a number of sub-committees each composed of representative(s) from the canals, canal carriers, war office, railway executive committee, and ministry of munitions. The Oxford was in the Southern sub-committee, whose canal representatives were W. Salt of the Birmingham & Warwick and J. W. Bliss of the Grand Junction; the latter's office at 21 Surrey Street, Strand, London WC2, were used for the meetings.[5]

The canals were eventually decontrolled as from 31 August 1920 and no further subsidy was paid after that date, but by virtue of section 3 of the Ministry of Transport Act of 1919 canals were able to increase their charges by 150 per cent from 31 July 1920.

Immediately the Oxford set about overcoming the arrears of maintenance particularly at the Oxford end where, by November in the following year, 1,230 tons had been dredged from Duke's cut over its length of ¼ mile and 35,000 tons over the 3 miles between Duke's Junction and Oxford. The boats carrying the spoil from the dredger took it to a point immediately above Duke's lock, where it was dumped into Duke's lake between the towing path and the railway embankment.[6]

Even such small wharves at Eynsham received much needed maintenance, the weighbridge there being reconditioned by Messrs Avery in 1910 for £15 and in the following year a new oak balance pole of 43 cubic feet was provided for Clay weir. The dredging of the Upper Thames in 1913, as part of the Thames Conservancy's programme, resulted in some boats having to lighten their cargoes before they could be got over the weir sill. The Oxford therefore made another weir 30yd from the river for £105 in the same year. This work was superintended by the father of Aubrey Jones, the late engineering foreman of the Napton–Oxford section. The two gates then served the purpose of a normal lock. Even so in times of flood it was a tricky job getting a pair of narrow boats across from the towing path side of the Thames to the entrance of the wharf stream; to help the wharfinger would send down all available men. In summer time the boats might have to wait for anything up to five hours tied up to a wall just inside the weir gate before the water rose sufficiently for them to travel the half mile up to the wharf. During 1924 repairs were carried out to the second weir gate and at the same time four concrete posts about 6ft high were sunk into the ground by the weir so as to form a narrow upright pen 5ft square, the tops and bottoms of the posts being linked by heavy iron rings the purpose being to provide a parking space for the weir paddles, so that they were not carried away by the flood water.[7]

No doubt the difficulties of getting boats into the wharf increased the boatmen's costs and also worsened the service. Therefore it is not surprising to find that about 1925 the last boat load of coal was taken to the wharf by John Skinner for John Juggins of the Talbot inn, the last surviving wharf trader, who also bred black retrievers and kept peacocks.

In 1928 the Oxford sold the wharf with the exception of the inn to Sugar Beet & Crop Driers Ltd for £600 upon which they erected a factory.[8] There is no evidence to show that any local farmers used the wharf for the unloading of sugar beet, but instead in 1930 the GWR obtained permission to put in a private siding.[9]

The inn at this time was leased to Hall's Oxford Brewery Ltd and it remained so till 1950 when the Docks & Inland Waterways executive sold the inn and its garden, which is beside the wharf stream, for £3,500.[10]

Over the years the Grand Junction had been buying up other

canals with a view to improving its trading position and finally
it got an Act in 1928 which authorised the purchase of the
Warwick & Napton and Warwick & Birmingham and as from
1 January 1929 it was known as the Grand Union.[11] One of the
main purposes behind this Act was the Grand Junction's intention to widen the canal all the way from Braunston to Birmingham. In August the new company decided to apply for a grant
under Section 2 of the Development (Loans, Guarantees and
Grants) Act, 1929, for the reconstruction scheme. Negotiations
were carried out with the Oxford regarding its 5 miles between
Braunston and Napton, ranging from outright purchase to running powers. The former was nearly agreed but fell through due
to difficulties in resolving the Oxford's property in that city, but
in the end the Grand Union had to be content with special powers
which were included within its Act of 1931. By this the Grand
Union had, as from 1 January 1932, the right to widen the Oxford
between Braunston and Napton. Between 1932 and 1947 the
Grand Union carried out a number of improvements on this
section in addition to general maintenance. As part of their policy
the canal between Braunston Junction and Napton Junction was
dredged to give a uniform depth of 5ft 6in. To prevent bank
erosion from the wash created by diesel driven narrow boats,
concrete piling was provided at many locations and this was
capped with concrete on which was inscribed the date installed,
depth of pile and permitted depth for dredging alongside the
piles. The Grand Union intended to use barges 12ft 6in wide over
this section when conveying traffic between London and Birmingham which necessitated many of the bridges being rebuilt.
Unfortunately they rebuilt the two which carried the main A425
Leamington Spa–Daventry road over the canal and perpetuated
two difficult turns for canal craft instead of making a new cut for
900yd alongside the road and thereby eliminating them.

Rates for traffic passing between the former Grand Junction
and the former Warwick & Napton now included passage over
the Oxford. The latter was to receive £900 per annum if the

tonnage did not exceed 82,500 tons; however if over, 1p per ton was to be paid for the first 22,500 tons, ⅔p per ton for the next 45,000 tons and ½p per ton for the rest. Once again the Oxford had been able to exert its influence and provide a satisfactory income by way of a bar-toll.

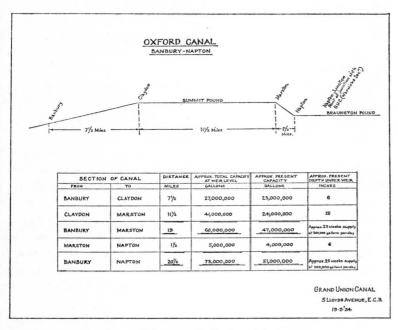

FIGURE 15. Water supply, Banbury–Napton, 1934

Every year the committee inspected the whole length of the canal and for this purpose in 1893 they had built for them an inspection launch called *Lady Godiva*. Usually the inspection started at Hawkesbury and the boat was steered by the engineer who must have got very black in the early days when it was powered by a steam engine with a copper boiler. Later on the Oxford replaced it by an internal combustion engine taken from a motor lorry.[12] To assist with the inspection Frederick Wood had made a number of chain survey books in 1830 which gave details of bridges, locks, mile posts, etc, and several of these are still in use today.

Ever since the canals had been decontrolled the Oxford had been allowed to charge up to 150 per cent above its standard rates, but by virtue of the Expiring Laws Continuance Act of 1934 this was to cease as from 31 December 1935. In consequence the Oxford promoted a Bill to rectify the position. It was introduced into the House of Commons on 30 January 1935 and as there were no petitions against it the Bill soon passed through all its stages and received the Royal Assent on 28 March.[13] Besides providing for the post-war level of rates to continue it allowed the Oxford to raise the minimum toll to 25p, borrow up to £10,000 and provide electric cable haulage for boats.

Whilst a canal could be modernised and be fully operational during most of the year, hard winters brought icing conditions which, if not tackled continuously, resulted in boats being frozen in sometimes for as much as ten weeks with the result that in Banbury boat crews used to go around the town begging with a miniature boat frozen in a block of ice. In addition, the Old Charitable Society set up a soup kitchen in a three-storey building in Calthorpe Street. Tradesmen would give vegetables and bones and voluntary helpers sold the soup at about 2½p a pint.[14]

The Oxford kept large icebreaking boats at Heyford and Napton which were pulled sometimes by ten or more horses with as many men as possible to rock the boat.[15] Small icebreakers were also kept at Banbury and at Thrupp, a delightful village 6 miles north of Oxford noted for its thatched cottages many of which were owned by boatmen.

Perhaps if there had been more powered craft on the Oxford the people who manned the icebreakers would have been taken off their normal work less frequently. In fact in the 1930s only about one in thirty boats on the southern part of the canal had an engine.[16] Coal fired steam-driven narrow boats had been in use on

Plate 29 Oxford–Worcester street wharf on the right and on the left under Worcester street bridge, New Road coal wharf, 1946

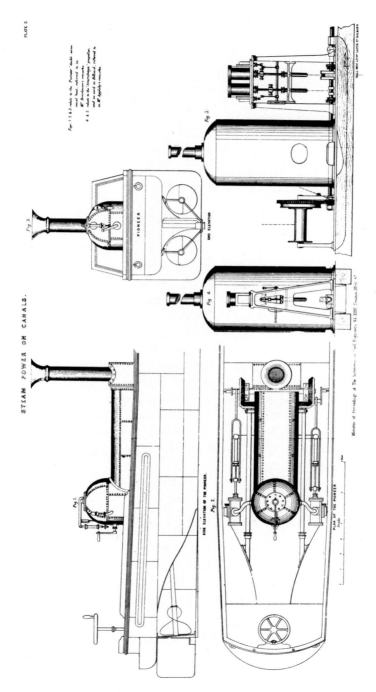

Plate 30 Details of Inshaw's tug *Pioneer* which worked on the northern part of the canal in the late 1860s

the canals since the middle of the last century, but the loss of 5 tons of cargo space coupled with the need for an engineman soon resulted in the steamers being discarded when diesel engines came into use. The last steamer made a trip in 1931 and found a resting place on a backwater at Hillmorton near Rugby in Warwickshire where she just rusted and rotted away. Right up to 1958 Joe Skinner, one of the last surviving owner boatmen (Number Ones), was still making his way from a colliery near Coventry to Banbury with a boat called *Friendship* pulled by a mule named Dolly, but the lack of towing path maintenance meant she had to walk through the water in many places and in consequence Dolly caught a cold and regretfully passed away.

In 1936 the Oxford realised the value of its land at Oxford forming Worcester Street and New Road wharfs and shortly afterwards sold it to Lord Nuffield, the founder of the Morris car works at Oxford, as a site for a new college. In the following year he passed it on to the university, but it was not till after World War II that work started on the site when the foundation stone was laid on 21 April 1949. The displaced coal merchants were transferred to Juxton Street wharf about ¾ mile west and a chain-operated ferry was established just west of Isis lock to enable the horses to transfer to the wharf from the towing path.

After the start of hostilities in 1939 the Oxford continued to run its own affairs as in World War I. The Government, however, soon felt the greatest use was not being made of the canals, so in 1941 Frank Pick was appointed to investigate and report upon the best steps to take. In his report to the Minister of War Transport he stated that, 'The most lucrative undertaking was the Oxford Canal which in 1938 and 1939 met its debenture and preference interest in full and paid 8% on its ordinary stock.' He then analysed the potential of each waterway and one of his recommendations was that the southern part of the Oxford which links the Grand Union with the Thames, should be fully restored, so that it could be used as an alternative route in the event of damage to the main route to London.

I

The Oxford was, of course, narrow compared with the Grand Union and also very muddy which made the going slow. What was worse, as evidenced by Susan Woolfitt who was one of the earliest canal boatwomen trained by the Ministry of War Transport when she took a load of coal down over five days to Oxford from Longford near Coventry in March 1945, was the fact that some of the lock walls bulged out as a result of frost thus effectively reducing the width below 7ft.[17]

Even so traffic still passed on the southern section though from the figures of loaded narrow boats passing during the week ended 14 June 1942 the preponderance was on the northern part: Hawkesbury Junction—199; Hillmorton—134; Napton Junction —102; Banbury—34; Duke's Junction—23.[18]

Coal traffic moved off the Oxford and on to the Grand Union for such destinations as Boxmoor, Berkhamsted, Camden Town, Croxley, Fenny Stratford, Hayes, Hatton, Harefield, King's Langley, Leighton Buzzard, Slough, Southall and Uxbridge. Coal also came down the Oxford to Fenny Compton, Cropredy, Banbury, Enslow, Wolvercote paper mill, Oxford and out on to the Thames to the Oxford electric works and Sandford paper mill 4 miles down river. Merchandise traffic only accounted for about 20 per cent of the movements, some of which came from far afield such as stores from Manchester for the RAF at Oxford brought down by Fellows Morton & Clayton. On the other hand the *Tweed* and *Gifford* owned by Thomas Clayton of Oldbury between them moved 43 tons of tar in specially constructed narrow boats twice a week from the Oxford gas works, situated on the Thames below Osney lock, to Banbury. Albert Beechey continued to steer these boats right up to 1955 when the gas works was closed.

Despite the efforts of the Central, and Regional Canal Committees, a war time organisation charged with making the best use of waterways, traffic declined and the following figures of coal boats unloaded at Oxford graphically show this trend.

Year	Boats		Year	Boats
1942	223		1950	19
1943	193		1951	19
1944	96		1952	30
1945	142		1953	16
1946	109		1954	10
1947	67		1955	18
1948	51		1956	16[19]
1949	40			

At Oxford the system for unloading coal boats was that as soon as a boat was expected the company employed six men from the Labour Exchange and paid them 30p each for unloading it. Wages however rose, so initially the company reduced the number to four and then to three, the fourth man being one of the boatmen. Even so the costs for unloading a boat, which normally carried about 25 tons of coal, rose from £1.80 to £6.50.

No. **2997**

....

Weighed at the Oxford Canal Company's Wharf.......................................

for M ....

Date		TONS.	CWT.	QRS.
	Gross Weight ..			
	Weight of Cart ..			
19	Net Weight ..			

FIGURE 16.   Weight ticket, 1946

Even whilst Banbury warehouse and lock were being bombed in September 1940, other people were looking towards better times and improved methods of water transport. One of these was J. F. Pownall who, in 1942, published *The Projected Grand Contour Canal* to connect with the estuaries and canals in England. He had made a detailed study of numerous maps and discovered that at a level of 310ft it would be possible to construct canals over long distances without the need for locks. One such canal he projected from the Manchester area on the same level joined the Coventry at Atherstone and thence along the Oxford avoiding the locks at Hillmorton, to join the Grand Junction and Warwick & Napton, and then down the side of the Avon valley and round the hill to Banbury. From this point it swung away from the Oxford through Witney towards Bristol. This was, no doubt, a remarkable and imaginative proposal which would certainly have reduced costs and improved transits considerably, but unfortunately the political climate was not right.

Following the end of the war new attitudes were held about transport, which culminated in the Transport Act of 1947 by which canals, railways etc, were nationalised forming a new body known as the British Transport Commission. As from 1 January 1948 the canals came under the control of the Docks & Inland Waterways Executive, the Oxford forming part of their Southern area.

Efforts were immediately made to overcome arrears of maintenance, but by 1952 the situation was becoming critical. In that year the southern section (Napton–Oxford) earned only £4,726 against an expenditure of £17,215—a loss of £12,489.[20] The disclosure of these figures prompted people to think that possibly the Docks & Inland Waterways Executive might be thinking of closing this section, though no official pronouncement had been made on the subject. Even so the Inland Waterways Association, whose object was to advocate the use, maintenance and development of inland waterways of the British Isles and in particular to advocate and promote the restoration to good order of every navigable waterway, had been chiding the Executive for a number of years and decided to hold a boat rally over the 1955 August Bank holiday at Banbury. The object was to draw the public's attention to the value of the Oxford both for commercial and pleasure craft, and to campaign in the most active manner against abandonment of the canal. About fifty boats attended including four working narrow boats sent by Thomas Clayton (Oldbury) Ltd and the Willow Wren Canal Carrying Co Ltd and well over 5,000 people enjoyed the rally in glittering sunshine. Earlier in the Town Halls of Oxford and Banbury over 300 people had enthusiastically protested against the possible threat.[21]

No apparent reaction took place, and the Oxford's figures for 1956 continued to paint a bleak picture: working expenses were £46,187, and receipts were £20,062, leaving a deficit of £26,125.[22]

To foster the growth of pleasure craft traffic on the canal the authority installed stand pipes for drinking water at strategic points and arranged for Banbury lock to be opened on Sundays. Previously the toll clerk tolled a bell at eight o'clock every week-day evening and then swung a heavy door across the towing path and locked up the lift bridge (No 165), thus effectively closing the canal until the following day, but if it was Saturday it remained closed till the Monday. At Grimsbury just north of Banbury the wooden lift bridge (No 162) was in need of repair, so to make it easier for users it was renewed in aluminium in 1959. On both the wooden and aluminium versions the balance arms are attached directly to the lifting platform and pivot by means of a tooth segment.

These are two other lift bridges on the canal which are not of the usual wooden construction. Besides the waters of the Cherwell half way between Oxford and Banbury there is a pre-Norman water mill at the picturesque village of Lower Heyford. The only road to the mill crosses the Oxford by a lift bridge (No 205). When the miller started to use traction engines to haul his waggons he found that the bridge was not strong enough. In consequence he had to tranship his load to and from carts on the

village side of the canal; therefore to avoid this cost he arranged
for the bridge to be renewed in iron. The mill changed hands in
1941 and by 1951 the wheel had ceased to be used.[23] The other
bridge is situated about 1½ miles above Oxford and connects
Osberton Radiators (now part of the Morris Oxford car works)
to another part of this complex. This one installed in 1930 is
power-operated and is worked from a nearby cabin by a member
of the work's staff. However, when the works is shut the lift
bridge is left open for the free passage of craft.

In 1957 British Transport Waterways started their 'Heart of
England Cruise' which operated between Oxford and Birmingham using a narrow boat converted by Thames Launch Works
Ltd and named *Water Rambler*. This was a luxury cruise for nineteen passengers and the tourists slept ashore in high grade hotels
and were conveyed to and from the boat in coaches. The whole
arrangement was considered to be something unique in travel
enjoyment. Light refreshments, drinks, lunches and teas were
served on the boat as the journey progressed. On the first day
passengers were conveyed by water between Kidlington wharf
and Aynho wharf; on the following day between Cropredy wharf
and Marston Doles wharf; the remaining three days were spent on
other canals. This service lasted until 1961 when the boat was
transferred elsewhere for day party work.

Other changes affected the 'old world' canal scenery. In 1959
Banbury Corporation published plans which envisaged the town
wharf becoming a bus station and the demolition of the picturesque, though 'below standard', land known as Factory Street,
long famous for its colony of retired working boatmen, and the
remarkable Strugglers Inn, a tough waterman's pub. The plans
were approved and in 1962 the remains of the bombed warehouse
and a sunken narrow boat called *The Rose and Betty* were covered
up.

Quite obviously the operating loss could not continue without
some financial contribution being forthcoming from elsewhere.
The British Waterways Board, an independent body, was set up

as from 1 January 1963 following the Transport Act of 1962. Under section 23 the Minister of Transport was enabled to make grants to meet revenue deficits and so the canals were able to continue in being.

The pleasure craft users of the canal were rapidly growing in numbers especially on the southern section which, being a pleasant rural canal, was soon to become the second most popular route for cruising in the whole system.

The former coal wharves at Stretton, Braunston, Aynho, and Oxford had a new lease of life when hire cruiser firms established businesses at these points. Even so the receipts allocated to the canal from pleasure craft did not exceed those from sale of water when a further report was published in 1965 which gave the following figures for the preceding year:

Section	Northern (£)	Southern (£)
Receipts—craft	1,296	1,398
Receipts—water	5,945	5,837
Receipts—other	1,094	3,226
TOTALS	8,335	10,461
Expenditure	31,770	35,829
Deficit	23,445	25,368[24]

The movement of powered craft through a canal with a comparatively narrow section and no bank protection soon results in silting, necessitating increased dredging, and the Oxford was no exception. Where money was available bank protection was undertaken and this usually took the form of concrete piles driven into the bank of the canal and held together by redundant rails purchased from British Railways, the dredgings being placed behind the piling to give it strength whilst the rails on curves also served as rubbing strips for boats which had difficulty in steering correctly round the corner. With the shortage of money not all the canal could be piled, so unfortunately the banks gave way sometimes where the canal passed over the countryside on an embankment. At Ansty on the northern part of the canal near Rugby, a 30ft high towing path embankment gave way in November 1963 washing out some 10,000 tons of sand and clay on to the adjoining land. To effect repairs it was necessary to construct a temporary dam around the breach to enable the clay puddle on the bed of the canal to be extended to the edge of the newly formed embankment which was rebuilt in reliable material. Although the canal at this point was reopened at the end of December, the final works were not completed till the following spring.[25] Almost at the same time the bank gave way near Newbold-on-Avon, only 11 miles away. In this instance only a minor breach occurred and it was possible to effect repairs quickly. Heavy rains soon produce excess water and whilst weirs had been placed along the canal at strategic points when it was built, the flow of water off the surrounding ground has altered over the years as a result of roads and housing estates being built which can result in flooding. Whilst the flooding of a field might not cause damage as it soon drained away, the flooding of property was quite another matter and to avoid this as far as possible a near weir was constructed at Hillmorton near Rugby in 1966 and another just south of Banbury.

One of the tasks given to the British Waterways Board when it was set up, was the production of a report setting out its thoughts on the future of the canal system having regard to the unsatisfactory financial position. The interim report was published in 1964 and it developed the theme that canals could serve other purposes besides transport. The Oxford was considered to have only a minor transport role between Hawkesbury Junction and Banbury, but on the other hand it had great potential in a possible pleasure cruising network, coupled with general recreation and amenity value such as for fishing and hiking.[26] The Board had in fact tried hiring out cabin cruisers from Juxton Street wharf, Oxford, but in 1963 these were transferred to Birmingham and Middlewich.

Pleasure craft on the Oxford were not generally licensed to go on to the Thames as well and therefore there was only limited movement between the two. The 7ft width restriction on the Oxford is often something of a deterrent to boats based on the Thames where a broader beam is possible.

Very little is known of the actual number of pleasure craft movements on the Oxford as toll offices have been closed, but by using the figures of the number of lock workings on the southern section during July 1970 some idea can be gained.

Marston Doles Top lock	607 workings
Claydon Top lock	593 workings
Nell Bridge lock	519 workings
Bakers lock	461 workings
Duke's cut stop lock	44 workings
Isis lock	141 workings[27]

The increasing numbers of pleasure craft use the canal mainly during the summer months unlike the former trading boats which used it all the year round and in consequence when a good dry season occurs, water shortages result. Another factor to take into account was the greater quantity of water required to pass a pleasure boat through a lock as compared with a loaded narrow boat; not only is less water displaced, but generally the pleasure craft was about half the length of a narrow boat. In 1972 the summer was exceptional and so was the movement of boats on the canal. So much so that the Area Engineer at Watford had to instruct his staff to lock up the section between Cropredy and Napton from 25 August between 18.00 and 08.00. This just sufficed for the remaining part of the cruising season but in October this section was closed altogether. The water level in Clattercote reservoir had dropped from 33ft to about 4ft, this being considered just sufficient for the survival of the fish. By this time also some pounds were 2ft 3in down and the 11 mile long summit pound between Claydon and Marston Doles was 9in down. In 1974 pumping was resorted to on the Napton flight, but this has proved very expensive when set against the actual pleasure craft receipts.

It is to be hoped that, with the present emphasis on the environment, ways and means will be found to keep the Oxford canal open for the benefit of anglers, hikers, boat users and all others who enjoy these popular waters.

Notes

NOTES TO CHAPTER 1 (*pages 7–29*)

1 8 Geo III, c 36
2 Wood, A. C., *The Diaries of Sir Roger Newdigate 1751–1806*
3 Ibid
4 *Jackson's Oxford Journal*, 25 October 1768
5 Wood, A. C., *The Diaries of Sir Roger Newdigate 1751–1806*
6 Report of a Committee appointed by Chamber of London to consider Bill for canal from Coventry to Oxford
7 Anon, *History of Inland Navigation*, 1769
8 9 Geo III, c 70
9 Oxford Canal subscription list, 1768
10 Pressnell, L. S., *Country Banking in the Industrial Revolution*, 1955
11 *Jackson's Oxford Journal*, 4 July 1774
12 15 Geo III, c 9
13 Information from N.E.D. Stevens of Oxford
14 Hogreve, H. L., *Canals of England*, 1777
15 Ibid
16 Weaver, C. P., 'The Arbury Canals', *Journal of the Railway & Canal Historical Society*, January & April 1970
17 Hogreve, H. L., *Canals of England*, 1777
18 Victoria County History—Oxfordshire, Volume X
19 Potts, W., *History of Banbury*, 1958
20 Weaver, C. P., 'The Arbury Canals', *Journal of the Railway & Canal Historical Society*, January & April 1970
21 Oxford Canal account book, 20 August 1778
22 Ibid
23 Hogreve, H. L., *Canals of England*, 1777

NOTES TO CHAPTER 2 (*pages 30–50*)

1 Oxford Siege papers, Bodleian Library, Oxford
2 Yarranton, A., *England's Improvement by Sea and Land*, 1677
3 Wood, A. C., *Sanderson Miller of Radway*, 1969
4 *Jackson's Oxford Journal*, 10 January 1764
5 Hogreve, H. L., *Canals of England*, 1777
6 Letter at Berkshire County Records Office, Reading
7 26 Geo III, c 20
8 25 Geo III, c 99

9   *Jackson's Oxford Journal*, 1 September 1787
10 Hobson, M. G., Oxford Council Acts 1752–1801
11 Pressnell, L. S., *Country Banking in the Industrial Revolution*, 1955
12 Information from J. J. Tawney of Berrick Salome
13 Hobson, M. G., Oxford Council Acts 1752–1801
14 39 Geo III, c 5
15 *Jackson's Oxford Journal*, 15 October 1791
16 Rusher, J. G., *Directory of Banbury*
17 Hartland, G. C. J., *The Boat Building Yard at Banbury*, 1969
18 Lawson, I.F., *Old Wharf—Adderbury*

NOTES TO CHAPTER 3 (*pages* 51–69)

1   Carter, H., *Wolvercote Mill*, 1957
2   Register of Leases at Blenheim Palace
3   Hadfield, Charles, *The Canals of South and South East England*, 1969
4   Chambers, Sir E., *Eynsham under the Monks*, 1936
5   Arkell, W. J., *Oxford Stone*, 1947
6   De Villiers, E., *Swinford Bridge 1769–1969*
7   Sills, J., *Report on the State of the Thames, Radcot bridge to Abingdon*, 1796
8   *Jackson's Oxford Journal*, 2 February 1800
9   40 Geo III, c 60
10 Agreement held at Blenheim Palace, 27 July 1802
11 Carter, H., *Wolvercote Mill*
12 Royal Commission on State of Thames, 1793
13 Letter at Blenheim Palace, 27 July 1791
14 Royal Commission on State of Thames, 1793
15 Stapleton, B., *Three Oxford Parishes*, 1893
16 Information from Controller, Wolvercote paper mill
17 *Jackson's Oxford Journal*, 2 February 1799
18 Mylne, R., *The State of the River Thames*, 1802
19 28 Geo III, c 51
20 Thames Commissioners minute book, 25 November 1805
21 Dalby, L. J., *The Wilts & Berks Canal*, 1971

NOTES TO CHAPTER 4 (*pages* 70–87)

1   Tombleson, *Thames*, 1834
2   Hadfield, Charles, *The Canals of South & South East England*, 1969
3   *Jackson's Oxford Journal*, 25 August 1792
4   Faulkner, A. H., *The Grand Junction Canal*, 1972
5   *Jackson's Oxford Journal*, 10 November 1792
6   *Northampton Mercury*, 1 September 1792
7   *Jackson's Oxford Journal*, 8 December 1792
8   Thames Commissioners minute book
9   Faulkner, A. H., *The Grand Junction Canal*, 1972
10 Letter from A. H. Faulkner
11 Faulkner, A. H., *The Grand Junction Canal*, 1972
12 Stockton Fortesque Collection
13 Faulkner, A. H., *The Grand Junction Canal*, 1972
14 Hadfield, Charles and Norris, John, *Waterways to Stratford*, 1962

15 Warwick & Napton Canal (committee) minute book, 7 June 1796
16 Ibid, 24 November 1797
17 Ibid, 13 June 1798
18 Patterson, A. T., *The Making of the Leicestershire Canals, 1766–1814*
19 Ibid
20 Truro, County Records Office

NOTES TO CHAPTER 5 (*pages* 88–110)

1   Warwick & Napton (committee) minute book, 14 December 1803
2   Faulkner, A. H., *The Grand Junction Canal*, 1972
3   Evidence of J. Ferguson before House of Commons committee on 1828 Oxford
    Bill
4   Warwick & Napton Canal (committee) minute book, 21 January 1833
5   Evidence given to House of Commons committee examining the Bill
6   Faulkner, A. H., *The Grand Junction Canal*, 1972
7   Map in the keeping of the Oxford C.R.O.
8   Letter to Charles Hadfield from A. V. Grantham, BWB
9   Oxford chain survey book
10 Ibid
11 Thames & Severn Canal tonnage book
12 Wilts & Berks Canal letter book
13 Oxford Canal letter book
14 Blenheim estate account book
15 Ibid
16 *Jackson's Oxford Journal*, 13 July 1833
17 Rusher, J. G., *Directory of Banbury*, 1837
18 Oxford Canal chain survey book.
19 Royal Commission on coal supplies, 1871
20 Report on Boatmen's chapel, Oxford City Library
21 Squires, T. W., *In West Oxford*, 1928
22 Fearon, J. H., 'Steam Navigation at Bodicote', *Cake and Cockhorse*, Banbury
    Historical Society, Summer 1968

NOTES TO CHAPTER 6 (*pages* 111–133)

1   E.M.S.P. The Two James's and the Two Stephensons, 1861
2   Hadfield, Charles and Norris, John, *Waterways to Stratford*, 1962
3   Steel, W. L., *History of the LNWR*, 1914
4   Crawford Dillon, R., *The Lord Mayor's Visit to Oxford*, 1846
5   Macdermot, E. T. (revised C. R. Clinker), *History of the Great Western Railway*,
    1964
6   Letter from P. Stevenson
7   Taylor, A. M., '*Gilletts' Bankers at Banbury and Oxford*, 1964
8   Minute book of the Oxford Canal, 19 June 1850
9   The Dew Collection
10 Minute book of the Buckinghamshire railway company, 11 July 1850
11 Ibid, 10 July 1851
12 9 Vic, c 203
13 Report on the State of the Thames, 1865
14 *Rugby Advertiser*, 18 August 1860

15   Minutes of proceedings of the Institution of Civil Engineers, *Steam Power on Canals*, Session 1866–7
16   *Rugby Advertiser*, 8 September 1860
17   Report on the State of the Thames, 1865
18   Evidence of J. Bossom before Royal Commission on River Thames, 1866
19   Carter, H., *Wolvercote Mill*, 1957
20   Extract from return submitted to Parliament in 1870
21   Letter from K. R. Clew
22   Evidence of Lord Desborough before Royal Commission on Canals and Inland Waterways, 1907
23   Faulkner, A. H., *The Grand Junction Canal*, 1972
24   Royal Commission on Canals and Inland Waterways, 1907

NOTES TO CHAPTER 7 (*pages 134–154*)

1   *Industrial Archaeology*, Vol 9, 1972
2   Victoria County History (Oxfordshire), Vol 10
3   Information from H. V. Gardner
4   *Journal on Canals and Waterways*, Vol I
5   Ministry of War Transport booklet, November 1918
6   Information from H. V. Gardner of Oxford
7   Information form G. Langford of Kidlington
8   Conveyance dated 16 July 1928
9   Information from British Railways, Western Region
10   Conveyance dated 6 July 1950
11   21 & 22 Geo V, c 90
12   Information from H. V. Gardner of Oxford
13   25 Geo V, c 15
14   Trinder, B. S., 'Further memories of Late Victorian and Edwardian Banbury', *Cake and Cockhorse*—Banbury Historical Society, Spring 1966.
15   Information from B. Hazell of Heyford
16   Banbury Health Department, Inspection book of Narrow-boats
17   Woolfitt, S., *Idle Women*, 1947
18   British Transport Historical Records
19   Information from E. K. Belsten of Oxford
20   Canals and Inland Waterways, Report of Board of Survey 1955
21   Bulletin 48, Inland Waterways Association, Autumn 1955
22   Report of the Committee of Inquiry into Inland Waterways, 1958
23   Busby, R. B., *Passing Thoughts in Idle Moments*, 1973
24   *The Facts About The Waterways*, British Waterways Board, 1965
25   Annual Report and Accounts, British Waterways Board, 1963
26   *The Future of the Waterways*, British Waterways Board, 1964
27   Information from British Waterways Board

Lock, Wharf and Distance Table—1904

	Miles	Fur-longs		Miles	Fur-longs
Hawkesbury Junction	o	o	Grimsbury Mill	49	2
Wyken Old Colliery Branch	1	4	Banbury Toll Office & Wharf	50	o
Wyken New Colliery Branch	1	6	Twyford Wharf	52	6
Stretton Wharf Branch	7	2	Nell Bridge Wharf	55	4
Brinklow Wharf Branch	7	6	Aynho Wharf	56	6
Fennis Field Lime Works Branch	9	4	Souldern Wharf	57	2
Normans & Walkers Works Branch	11	o	Somerton Wharf	59	o
Newbold Wharf	11	4	Upper Heyford Mill	61	2
Rugby Wharf Branch	12	4	Lower Heyford Mill	62	2
Brownsover Wharf	13	o	Washford Hill Quarries	66	2
Brownsover Mill	13	4	Ensors Mill Lock	66	6
Clifton Mill Branch	14	o	Shipton Weir Lock	69	3
Willoughby Wharf	21	o	Langford Lane Wharf	71	o
Branch to Grand Junction	22	6	Roundham Lock	71	6
Shuckburgh Wharf	26	2	King's Bridge Wharf	73	4
Napton Junction	27	6	Duke's Lock	74	o
Napton Wharf	28	6	Duke's Cut Branch	74	o
Napton Brickworks	29	o	Drewett's Wharf	74	5
Napton Bottom Lock	30	o	Wolvercote Lock	74	6
Napton Top Lock	31	6	Wolvercote Wharf	74	7
Claydon Top Lock	42	6	Frenchay Road Wharf	75	7
			Hayfield Hutt Wharf	76	o
			Juxton Street Wharf	76	6
			Isis Lock	77	o
			New Road Wharf	77	4

Branch to Wyken Old Colliery	2 furlongs, 9 chains
Branch to Wyken New Colliery	3 furlongs, 3¼ chains
Branch to Stretton	2 furlongs
Branch to Fennis Field	4 furlongs
Branch to Newbold Limeworks	1 mile, 1 furlong
Branch to Rugby Wharf	1 furlong, 8¾ chains
Cosford Branch	1 mile, 2 furlongs, 2½ chains
Clifton Mill Branch	3 furlongs, 5 chains
Branch to Napton Engine	4 furlongs
Duke's cut Branch	6 furlongs

Acts of Parliament

9 Geo III Cap	70	dated 21 April	1769
15 Geo III Cap	9	dated 30 March	1775
26 Geo III Cap	20	dated 11 April	1786
34 Geo III Cap	103	dated 23 May	1794
39 Geo III Cap	5	dated 21 March	1799
47 Geo III Cap	9	dated 25 July	1807
48 Geo III Cap	3	dated 11 March	1808
10 Geo IV Cap	48	dated 14 May	1829
25 Geo V Cap	15	dated 28 March	1935

K

Bibliography

WHILST no general history of any length has previously been written on the Oxford canal, researchers will find that the under-mentioned books will have a certain proportion of interesting reading matter on the canal.

Anon. *History of Inland Navigation* (1768)

Broadbridge, S. R. *The Birmingham Canal Navigation* (1974)

Faulkner, A. H. *The Grand Junction Canal* (1972)

Hadfield, Charles and Norris, John. *Waterways to Stratford* (1962)

Hadfield, Charles. *The Canals of the East Midlands* (2nd ed 1970)

Hadfield, Charles. *The Canals of South and South East England* (1969)

Hobson, M. G. *Oxford Council Acts 1752–1801* (1961)

Hogreve, J. L. *The Canals of England* (1777)

Macdermot, E. T. (revised C. R. Clinker). *History of the Great Western Railway* (1964)

Maggs, C. G. *The Midland and South Western Junction Railway* (1967)

Marshall, C. F. D. *History of British Railways down to 1830* (1938)

Moreau, R. E. *The Departed Village* (1968)

Mylne, R. *Report on the Navigation of the Thames above Oxford* (1802)

Mylne, R. *Report on the Navigation of the Upper Thames between Lechlade and Whitchurch* (1791)

Nock, O. S. *British Railways at War* (1971)

Pigot, J. *Directory* (1842)

Pick, F. *Report on Canals and Inland Waterways* (1941)

Potts, W. *History of Banbury* (1958)

Pressnell, L. S. *Country Banking in the Industrial Revolution* (1955)
Priestley, J. *Historical Account of Rivers and Canals* (1831)
Rees, A. *State of the Canals* (1806)
Rolt, L. T. C. *Narrow Boat* (1944)
Rusher, J. G. *Directory of Banbury* (1837)
Smith, G. *Our Canal Population* (1875)
Squires, T. W. *In West Oxford* (1928)
Stapleton, B. *Three Oxford Parishes* (1893)
Steel, W. L. *History of the LNWR* (1914)
Taylor, A. M. *'Gilletts' Bankers at Banbury and Oxford* (1964)
Wood, A. C. *The Diaries of Sir Roger Newdigate 1751-1806* (1962)
Wood, A. C. *Sanderson Miller of Radway* (1969)
Yarranton, A. *England's Improvement by Sea and Land* (1677)

Acknowledgements

THE writing of this book is the result of research work done over the last two decades. Much of it has been carried out by fellow members of the Railway & Canal Historical Society. In particular I wish to thank Kingsley Belsten, Ken Parrott and Brian McKinnell.

Numerous depositories have been consulted including the County Records Offices of Oxfordshire, Berkshire, Gloucestershire, and Warwickshire, the Bodleian Library at Oxford, the British Library Board both at Bloomsbury and Colindale, London, not forgetting the Marlborough family records at Blenheim Palace, Woodstock; all of whom most willingly made their various records available for inspection.

The former British Transport Historical Records office at Paddington held a large number of the basic records of the Oxford canal company and to all the staff who were employed there, I express my grateful thanks.

The Curator of the Waterways Museum at Stoke Bruerne beside the Grand Junction and many other persons employed by British Waterways have all been most helpful. Through the medium of the Banbury Historical Society's journal *Cock & Cakehorse* and its members I have been able to learn about the economic history for the area as a background to this work.

The translation of the Oxford portion of Hogreve's *Canals of England* from the eighteenth-century German MS, by Mrs Wilson of Woking, has produced information hitherto unrecorded in Britain.

Lastly I must give my thanks to Alan Faulkner who has read my original MS and made many helpful comments which have been embodied into this work.

For the photographs I am indebted to British Waterways, Stoke Bruerne for permission to reproduce the following: plates 1, 2 and 8; Oxford City Libraries, from the Taunt collection, by permission of the library committee, plates 21, 22 and 23; the Dew collection, plate 12; K. G. Parrott Esq, plate 6; Aerofilms, plate 11; the Ashmolean Museum, Department of Western Art, Oxford, plate 24; B. S. Trinder Esq, plate 28; *Oxford Mail*, plate 25; Rugby Public Library, plates 4 and 5; T. H. Maggs Esq, plate 3; Controller, Wolvercote paper mill, plate 19; Royal Commission Historical Monuments (England), plates 20 and 26; A. R. Mowbray & Co Ltd, plate 37; Bodleian Library, Oxford, plate 29; Institution of Civil Engineers, plate 30.

For maps and illustrations in the text my thanks are due to the British Library Board for the following: Figs 2, 3 and 6; County Archivist, Oxfordshire, Figs 5, 8, 10 and 12; County Archivist, Warwickshire, Fig 9; B. S. Trinder Esq, Fig 11; the Dew collection, Fig 13; British Waterways, Figs 14 and 15.

Index

References to illustrations are printed in bold type